Our kind of age
needs
a new kind of church
and a new kind of church
needs
a new kind of people
and a new kind of people
needs
a new kind of lifestyle
and this is what
"Rap" is all about.

Rap

a mini course in CHRISTIAN LIFESTYLE

by Lyman Coleman

with special articles by
Bill Milliken, Wally Howard, Don Williams

photography by Gene Wieland Jr.,
Joel Strasser and Wally Howard

art and design by Bob Blewett

CR **CREATIVE RESOURCES**
a division of **WORD, INC., WACO, TEXAS**

You are invited
to take part
in a risky search into
the meaning
of Christian lifestyle.

For a minimum of
six weeks (or sessions)
you will work
together
as a team
around a common discipline
of personal inventory
and group sharing.

All you need
is a healthy dissatisfaction
with your own lifestyle
and the courage
to do something about it.

**MY CONTRACT
WITH GOD
AND THE MEMBERS OF MY GROUP**

For the next few weeks
I agree
to take part
in an experiment
in Christian community
with the others in this group.
I pledge
to give priority to the group meetings,
to share responsibility for the leadership, and
to give my support to the others
in the group.

Signed: _____

Date: _____

here's how

The Relational Labs are a complete course in human relations, offering small groups a basis for building meaningful relationships on a depth human level based upon the latest concepts in group process, self discovery and behavioral psychology.

Relational Labs

Take your choice!

There are
three parallel tracks
in this course
(each with six sessions)
giving you
the option of
three different levels
of relationships
to choose from
depending upon the interest
and concern
of the group.

Lab 1: **Getting Acquainted.** You will get acquainted in small "family" groupings that will serve as the basis for interaction during the rest of the course.   *(page 26)*

Lab 2: **What Makes Me Tick.** Through a personal inventory, you will evaluate the drives in your life and share them in your small group.   *(page 27)*

Lab 3: **My Family Portrait.** You will evaluate your present family relationships and share your insights with a small group.   *(page 29)*

Lab 4: **A Fantasy Trip.** You will analyze the priorities and values in your present lifestyle and share the results in your small group.   *(page 30)*

Lab 5: **Give a Vacation.** By planning a fantastic vacation for each one in your small group you will share your hopes and dreams for them.   *(page 31)*

Lab 6: **An Appreciation Party.** This celebration allows you to express your appreciation for the others in your small group by creating a symbolic gift out of Play-Doh for each of them.   *(page 32)*

The Spiritual Encounters are a complete course in relational Bible study, providing a series of Reflection Questionnaires that help you to relate the Scripture to your own experience, based on the latest concepts in educational psychology.

The Enabling Sessions are a complete course in inductive Bible study, providing a series of small-group studies to reinforce the Relational Labs and Spiritual Encounters with further study of Scripture, based on the latest concepts in inductive Bible study and group dynamics.

Spiritual Encounters

Enabling Sessions

And you can
take your pick
from any
of the following
plans
for scheduling
the course.

the take-it-easy plan

This plan is designed for groups who need to get to know each other on a human level and to relate to each other as persons. This plan would take a group through the six human relations labs in Track One first and then move on to the spiritual encounters in Track Two after they have gotten to know each other.

Session one....... Relational Lab 1
Session two....... Relational Lab 2
Session three..... Relational Lab 3
Session four...... Relational Lab 4
Session five...... Relational Lab 5
Session six....... Relational Lab 6
Session seven..... Spiritual Encounter 1
Session eight..... Spiritual Encounter 2
Session nine...... etc.

the study-as-you-go plan

This plan is designed for groups who need to go beyond the human level in their relationships and are willing to commit themselves to each other as a spiritual community. Here, you would move laterally across the three tracks, taking the first session in each track in the first three sessions. Then, move to the second session in each track, etc., throughout the program.

Session one....... Relational Lab 1
Session two....... Spiritual Encounter 1
Session three..... Enabling Session 1
Session four...... Relational Lab 2
Session five...... Spiritual Encounter 2
Session six....... Enabling Session 2
Session seven..... Relational Lab 3
Session eight..... Spiritual Encounter 3
Session nine...... etc.

the open-ended plan

This plan is designed for mature groups who are capable of evaluating their own progress and can decide upon their own course of action. Here, the group would start out with Lab 1 and decide after the lab if they feel they need another lab for "group building" — or are ready to move on to the Spiritual Encounters. Then, at the close of the second session, you would evaluate your progress and plan accordingly.

Session one....... Relational Lab 1
Session two....... Lab 2 or
                   Spiritual Encounter 1
Session three..... Elective choice
Session four...... Elective choice
Session five...... Elective choice
Session six....... Elective choice
Session seven..... Elective choice
Session eight..... Elective choice
Session nine...... etc.

how to organize

Radical differences in background,
philosophy and lifestyle
in the make up of a small group
can be an asset
as long as there is a basic commitment
to each other
for the duration of the course.

a group

A group can consist of any combination: all men, all women, couples, young people, youth and adults together. In the same group, you might have the young and the old, the educated and uneducated, the "way out" and the "way in." In fact, radical differences in background, philosophy and lifestyle in the make up of a small group can be an asset as long as there is a basic commitment to each other for the duration of the course.

The course provides the opportunity for the group to get to know each other in the first few sessions. Half of the fun is in discovering each other as fellow human beings — in search of God.

To find each other, here are a few suggestions:

1. start with yourself

The hardest person you will have to convince is yourself. After you are thoroughly convinced that you need a small group to belong to, you will be able to find others. There is something contagious about a person who is honest enough to admit his need for others.

2. enlist a friend

The chances are that you know of someone else who would be interested in belonging to a small group. Get together with this person and share your own need for a group. Show him this workbook. Ask him if he has the same need. All it takes is for someone to say, *Hey, I'm hurting for a group of people where I can relate and belong! How about you?*

3. plan a "get together"

Invite anyone who might be interested to a "coffee" in your home. Use some of the ideas in the Relational Labs (pages 25-33) to get them talking in groups of four. Without even realizing it, the guests will find themselves "caught up" in the warmth of a community of love — enjoying the fellowship and experiencing a little bit of the meaning of "koinonia."

4. explain the course

Once a person has experienced a taste of "koinonia", he is going to want more. This will give you the opportunity to explain the various possibilities in this course.

Don't shortchange the group by making the group just another social club where people can come or go as they please. One of the prerequisites of a group is "togetherness." This means wedding yourselves together as a team for a specific period of time and helping each other reach a common objective. (See the next two chapters.)

You owe it to the prospects to clearly lay out the minimum conditions in this course. Namely,

(a) You will meet together once a week or once every other week for six to eight weeks. (After this, you have the option of continuing as a group for another twelve weeks if you want to.)

(b) You will select your own agenda for each session from the various options that are available (pages 6-7). Track One offers you six human relations labs. Track Two offers you six spiritual growth labs. Track Three offers you six Bible study labs. You can stick with one track or switch back and forth.

(c) You rotate the leadership within the group, each person taking his turn. There is no outside reading or homework required, but the first part of each sessions starts off with a brief creative exercise to get you involved

in the content of the session.

(d) Everyone will need this workbook to belong to the group. It is highly recommended that each person pay for his own book.

5. decide on a time and place

The group can meet any time in the week and any place in the community. Men's groups often meet for breakfast. Ladies' groups for tea. Couples' groups for coffee in the evening. Some groups meet during the regular meeting hour of Sunday School — or after church at one of their homes. The only condition is a minimum of 60 minutes for the actual sharing time, followed if possible by a free period in which the small groups can continue for a few minutes if they want to.

The place can be a local restaurant, an office, one of your homes or a different home each week, or even one of the rooms at church. The only condition is chairs that can be rearranged in small clusters for the sharing period at each session. (This is especially important if you have more than six in your group.)

6. select your agenda

As we have mentioned before, there are three different tracks you can run on (pages 6-7). Track One provides a series of human relations labs for "group building." Track Two provides a series of study encounters for spiritual growth and awareness as a group. Track Three provides a series of inductive Bible studies for reinforcing the personal and group experience in the other two tracks.

If you don't know each other, you will probably want to spend a couple

continued on page 14

here's

how to conduct a practice session

Are you all fired up about starting a small group — but don't know anybody else to join? How about putting on a practice session for all of your friends?

It's simple. Get your friends together and do one of the labs on pages 25-33 — and let your friends decide for themselves if they want to continue in the course.

The perfect atmosphere for the get-together is a social. Don't worry about the fancy frills. Just serve them a cup of coffee and ask them to sit down in groups of four — with someone they don't know very well but would like to know. If you happen to have enough card tables, great. Otherwise, arrange the chairs in groups of four.

Then, explain the instructions for the lab as though you were the leader in the lab. Without realizing it, the guests will find themselves involved in a beautiful experience of sharing with each other.

After the session, explain a little bit about the meaning of small groups and invite anyone who is interested in belonging to an experimental group for six or eight weeks to speak to you afterward. You are going to be amazed at the readiness of your friends to sign up.

of sessions getting acquainted in the human relations labs. Then, once you have "become a group," you may want to switch tracks and get into something deeper.

You will find the actual instructions for each session in the middle of this book. A quick glance at the "purpose" at the beginning of each session will give you a good idea of what to expect in the session.

7. keep an empty chair

Three or four people are enough to start a group, and it will grow in number if the group is functioning properly.

As the group grows, you will have to sub-divide the group into smaller groups of four at each session so that everyone is able to participate in the sharing experience.

At all costs, avoid the temptation to think of yourselves as a closed corporation. This can lead to all sorts of problems and will eventually lead to the death of the group.

Newcomers should have no problem coming into the group in the middle of the course, because the nature of the sharing is "personal experience." In fact, newcomers will keep the group fresh.

8. find a mission

Once you have started to discover the secret of "koinonia," you will want to find ways of sharing your experience with others. If you don't, something is wrong.

The mission you decide upon must grow out of your experience as a group if it is to be your own. Therefore, we have not prescribed the particular form of mission for you, but we have given you some direction in the study assignments in Track Three.

In the back of this book you will find stories of what some people have done as a natural outreach of their community concern. You should read over these stories for ideas and decide what you are going to give yourself to as a group.

"A servant people inevitably becomes a witnessing community. When we identify ourselves with the sufferings of others who have no observable claim on us, the world takes note. . . . The leaven which was hid cannot be concealed any longer; the light is seen to be shining in the darkness; there is a community as obvious as a city set on a hill."

Robert Raines
Reshaping the Christian Life

15

how to work together as

Like a three-legged stool,
every group
has three supports.
Take away any one of the three
and the whole thing
collapses.

There are three ingredients vital
to a small group: (1) personal
growth, (2) group building, and
(3) task or mission.

Personal growth has to do with the
whole matter of discovering yourself
as a person — your unique gifts,
strengths and weaknesses; your
spiritual and intellectual formation,
etc. In a word, to come to terms with
yourself as an individual: to be a
"whole" person.

Group building has to do with the
matter of becoming a team — a
community of love, trust and
acceptance where you feel a part of
each other and can minister to each
other as the body of Christ. In a word,
to discover the meaning of "koinonia."
We will have more to say about this
later on. But let us underscore something right here. *A group does not
become a group merely by sitting
down together.* It takes time to become
a group — and it takes caring, sharing,
forgiving and affirming. Just like
marriage.

Task or *mission* has to do with the
matter of taking responsible action
individually and collectively to share

a group

TWO VIEWS OF GROUP FLOW

To make sure that a small group maintains a balance between study and action, personal growth and group growth, introspection and mission, etc., you should develop a schedule in which the various needs are taken care of: (1) individual self-discovery and growth, (2) group formation and maintainance, and (3) outreach and mission.

There are two ways to look upon the schedule. The first might be called a *Static View of Group Flow. In this view, the time for each session is divided equally between: (a) personal growth and study, (b)* group building, and (c) task or mission and prayer.

The second view might be called a Dynamic View of Group Flow. *In this view, the entire period that a group has agreed to run is looked upon as a package, and the majority of the time at the beginning of the course is given over to group building (getting to know each other in depth). Then, once the group has learned how to work together as a team, they can get into the matter of study, mission and action.*

Both views have their advantages. However, if the group has agreed to meet for several weeks together, the second view holds out the chance for more significant results.

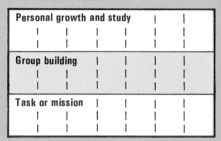

A. STATIC VIEW

Personal growth and study

Group building

Task or mission

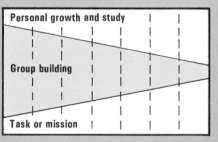

B. DYNAMIC VIEW

Personal growth and study

Group building

Task or mission

your life with others. This can be anything from a weekend lay-witness mission to an involvement in race relations, but it should grow out of your life together.

a happy balance

The trick is to keep all three of these emphases in perspective. Unfortunately, a lot of small groups will emphasize one of the ingredients to the total exclusion of the others. For instance, one group will spend all of their time in study and prayer and end up with spiritual indigestion — while another group will spend all of their time sitting around trying to figure out what to do about poverty and end up spiritually bankrupt.

One possible solution to this problem is to assign an equal amount of time at every session to each emphasis: (a) 20 minutes to personal growth and study, (b) 20 minutes to group building and sharing, and (c) 20 minutes to task discussion and prayer. This will give a group a balance, but forces a group into study and mission before they have become a group.

A second possibility is to look upon the six to ten weeks that the group

have committed themselves to as a
package and apportion the largest
amount of time at the beginning of the
course to group building. Then,
once the group has become a group,
spend less and less time on group
building and more and more time on
personal growth and mission.

The special box on page 18 describes
these two views.

becoming a group

There are three stages in group building
that a group must go through before
it is really a group: (a) history-giving,
(b) affirmation, and (c) worship.

History-giving means feeding into
the group the basic data that the
group needs to know about each
other — past, present and future.
This means giving each person a chance
to share his personal concerns, fears,
failures, hopes and dreams; the
significant events, people and places
in his life; his spiritual background,
his emotional ups and downs and
his present hurts and joys. Any
group that fails to take the time to
get to know each other in depth will
find themselves constantly back-
tracking, infighting and
misunderstanding.

Affirmation grows out of the first
stage of history-giving and develops
in exact proportion to the level of
openness and honesty in the
history-giving stage. Affirmation
means responding as a community
of love, trust and acceptance to the
particular needs, hurts, wants, fears
and hopes, joys and dreams that
were brought into the open in the
first stage. This means going the

second mile with each other, "hearing
out" a brother that needs to get
something off his chest, reaching out
and literally "bearing up" each other
as a community of love. It is at this
stage that a group will start to discover
a little bit about the meaning of
"koinonia."

Worship automatically follows when
"koinonia" happens — spontaneously
and at times hilariously. Worship as a
community means responding to the
Spirit of God collectively . . . *"in one
mind, in singleness of heart"* . . . as
the Christian community in the Book
of Acts was described.

the three tracks

This is where the value of the three
tracks in this course comes in. It
gives you the chance to map out
your own agenda as a group and
to switch tracks if you feel that you
need a different emphasis.

For instance, Track One is essentially
a "group building" track. Track Two
is essentially a "personal growth"
track, and Track Three is a "mission
study" track. If your group is running
on Track One and you have established
a real spirit of "koinonia" after two or
three sessions, you can switch tracks
and get into some study in Track
Two or Three that will help you to
check your experience with Scripture.
Then, if you find the group bogging
down in study in Track Two or Three,
you can switch back to Track One
for some more group building.

With the three tracks, there is no
reason why you cannot discover a
happy balance between personal
growth, group building and mission.

THE THREE PHASES OF GROUP BUILDING

1. INDIVIDUAL HISTORY-GIVING

Who am I?
My strengths
Concerns

Fears
Hopes
Dreams

2. GROUP AFFIRMATION

Who you are
Your strengths
Gifts

Qualities
Positive impressions

3. WORSHIP

Celebration
Communion
Commissioning

how to enable the best in each other

To call forth the best in each other is the goal of a small group—but unfortunately few groups know how to do this.

The purpose of a small group is to help each one in it to reach his full potential. This is a game where everyone must win — everyone must come out on top.

And the way this is done is called *enabling*. The word *enable* means to pull forth from, to call forth, to allow to emerge, to realize the potential of. This is what a small group is all about.

Most people realize about 10 percent of their potential. The other 90 percent lies beneath a pile of fears, failures, broken dreams, painful childhood memories and guilt feelings that add up to make us feel that we are not going to make it in anything we do. And with that kind of outlook, we definitely will not.

This is where a small group comes in. In the company of sympathetic, caring, loving people, we are able to open up and talk about our hangups and fears as well as our hopes and dreams for the future. Instead of getting negative feedback from others, we get positive feedback — affirmation. *I affirm you in this venture . . . I affirm this gift . . . I affirm this task in your life . . .* Slowly, the affirmation from those we have come to love and trust overcomes the negative feelings we have fed into our computers over the years . . . and we are able to say, *I am worthwhile . . . I have unique gifts . . . I can accomplish the thing . . . I will try again. . . .*

Three levels of sharing

All of us yearn for fellowship where we can feel a oneness and call forth the best in each other. In a word, to minister to one another as the Body of Christ. Before this can happen, however, we must run the risk of being known — and this is scary. We

21

are afraid that if people find out who we are inside they will reject us. So, to cover up the real person inside, we talk about the weather, about football, about the latest joke in town. And all the while, down deep inside, we are crying out for love.

But love is the result of knowledge, and knowledge comes when we are willing to let another person know us as we really are.

One of the best ways to bring a group face to face with their level of commitment to each other is to ask them to evaluate their experiences according to the three levels of sharing: (1) mouth-to-mouth, (2) head-to-head and (3) heart-to-heart. The mouth-to-mouth sharing is simply conversational doodling — the weather, football, etc. The head-to-head sharing is more serious in that it is exchanging ideas and concepts — but the exchange is strictly as ideas detached from the persons. The heart-to-heart sharing, on the other hand, lets the other person know where *you* stand in relation to ideas and how you *feel* about them on the inside. The heart-to-heart sharing might be referred to as communing . . . and communing is the stuff from which community is born.

A small group can very easily sit and play verbal volleyball with each other, and this is okay. But don't expect real Christian community in this atmosphere. Community happens when one person dares to say, *This is the way I feel . . . In all honesty, this is where I am . . . This is me . . . see me . . . know me . . . I want to be a part of you and I want you to be a part of me . . . I want you to know me . . . I want to know you — deeply.* When this starts to happen in a group, watch out.

"The inner life of many people is simply vacant. They may have once had a faith to give life coherence and meaning, but the widespread materialism around them and the corrosions of secularistic philosophy in education have robbed them of it. So we fill our hands and our time with all kinds of activity to make us forget, while our souls are empty of those convictions and standards which alone give life purpose and direction. People turn to pleasure, business, radio and television, sex, drink, drugs — anything to fill the emptiness within."

Sam Shoemaker

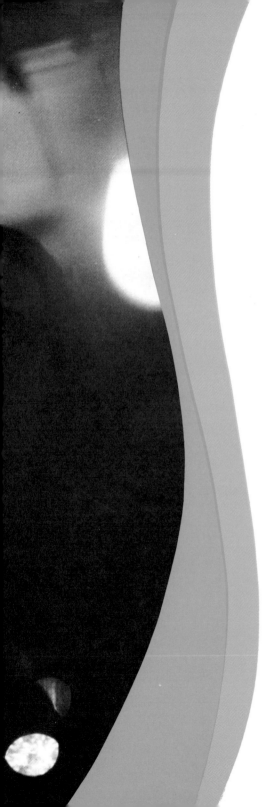

Four tips to keep in mind

When one person in a group takes the leap and decides to let the others in on his life, the group is under a real obligation as the Body of Christ to be the ministering servants to this person.

First, don't interrupt. Keep your mouth shut — and let the person talk. The chances are that he has never had anyone in his life to really listen to him. The greatest thing we can offer is our ears. Many times this is all a person needs — and wants. Remember, the greatest counselors say the least.

This may mean dispensing with the agenda in your small group and giving over the entire session to a person who needs to share how he is really feeling and hurting on the inside. After all, the purpose of the group is to *enable each other*, not to cover the agenda. The leader of the group should be sensitive at this point and be prepared to adjust the schedule. He can ask, *Have you said all that you have to say about this?* or, *Would you like to add anything before we go on?* or, *Are you trying to tell us something?* These questions are enabling questions that let a person go a little deeper in his sharing.

Second, don't probe. There is a thin line between listening and probing, but it is a very important one. To listen is to enable a person to say all that he wants to say. To probe is to make a person share what he does not want to say — and should not reveal at this time. A probing question takes the initiative away from the person who is sharing — and this is bad.

If someone in the group starts to probe, the leader should step in immediately with, *Let's let Bill tell it the way he sees it*, or, *Why don't we give Bill a chance to finish what he has to say?*

Third, don't give advice. The cheapest thing in the world is advice. Very often, the person with the least information is the most free in his advice — and the results are disastrous. If someone in the group has had a similar experience, he can share his experience — without telling the other person what he ought to do.

If someone in the group starts to give advice, the leader should break in immediately and say, *Why don't you share your experience but let Helen make her own application?* or, *Let's hold off on the advice and stick just to our own experience!*

Fourth, don't judge. If the group really is one, some sensitive areas of disagreement in lifestyle, theology and outlook are going to come up. Here is the place where love is going to be put to the test. When you violently disagree with another person, can you give him the right to his own viewpoint? Can you not only affirm him, but release him to be himself, to think as he must? This does not mean giving in or making concessions. This means telling him, *I cannot see it the way you see it . . . but I love you and I accept you just as you are and with what you believe.*

When this kind of listening, caring, loving, accepting thing happens in a group, you will know it . . . and so will everyone else. This is what it is all about.

Remember, "to enable" is to call forth the best in another person, to see the best in him, to affirm the best in him. Are you an enabler?

My Family Portrait

Relational Labs

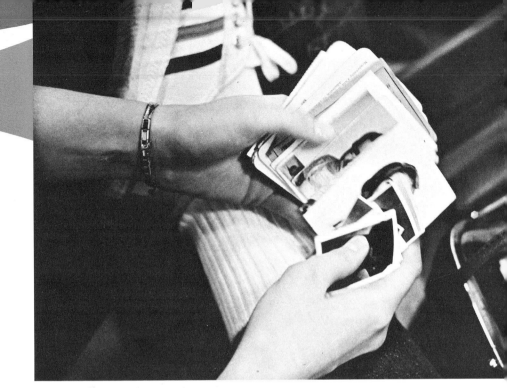

Getting Acquainted

Purpose: To enable you to get acquainted in small groups and start building relationships of trust and confidence that will prove invaluable in later sessions.

Setting: A casual, informal atmosphere, with people sitting on the floor or in chairs that can be moved close together for groups of two, four, eight.

Time: 45 to 60 minutes, with a free period at the close for groups who want to continue a little longer. If you are able to give 90 minutes to this session, you may be able to include Spiritual Encounter 1 (see page 36).

Materials required: A workbook and pencil for everyone.

Leadership: The role of leader should rotate within the class to a different person for each session. He should be assigned the week before so that he will be prepared to explain the procedure in his own words, model examples from his own life and collect any materials needed.

PROCEDURE

The session is divided into three "group building" sharing exercises: (1) Pearls of Great Price — with everyone working individually and then in groups of two, with people who do not know each other getting together, (2) Swap Game — for groups of four, with each group of two finding a group they do not know, (3) Two Questions — in groups of four or eight, with each group of four doubling, if possible, with a group they do not know.

Time limits are suggested for each exercise, but play it by ear here; if there is not time for the third exercise, it is okay.

Pearls of Great Price (15 minutes)

The object of this exercise is to enable you to explain to one other person the significant possessions and values in your present lifestyle.

1. In silence, look over the possessions you have with you (or on you) and select three things that you would classify as "very valuable" to you either in themselves or as symbols of your lifestyle. For instance, you might pick a *picture* of your girl friend as a symbol of relationships in your life; a *key* to your motorcycle as a symbol of ego satisfaction; one of your *sandles* as a symbol of your lifestyle of freedom.

2. The leader will call time in three minutes.

3. Explain your selection, including the *why*, to someone you do not know very well. The *why* is very important. For instance, you might select a *prayer medal* as one of your most valuable

possessions — not because it is valuable in itself, but because it symbolizes the significance of God in your lifestyle.

If there is time, rank the items in order of priority in your life; 1, 2, 3.

Swap Game (15 minutes)

Here you evaluate your present lifestyle and share two things: (a) something you would like to add to your lifestyle, (b) something you would like to subtract from your present lifestyle.

1. Each team of two joins another team, preferably persons they do not know very well.

2. Close your eyes for a couple of minutes and imagine yourself stepping into a huge department store that specializes in every area of lifestyle: attitudes, values, relationships, vocation, habits. Pretend that the store manager says to you, *Select one thing in this store for yourself. It can be anything. But there is a condition. You must leave something that you presently have.*

For instance, you might visit the attitudes department and pick up a box marked *Enthusiasm*. Or, you might stop at the values department and pick out a box labeled *People First*. Or, you might go to the relationships department and choose a large package of *Openness*.

3. Then you might decide to leave *a fear of nonconformity*, or, *a sense of personal inadequacy*, or, *a hot temper*.

4. In the groups, each person in turn shares the swap he made at the store.

Note: It will be very effective if the leader shares with the entire class what he would swap — in all honesty. This will set the pace for openness.

Two Questions (15 to 30 minutes)

In this exercise you pinpoint the motivating forces in your life and relate your insights to others.

1. If only 15 minutes are left, stay in groups of four; if there are 30 minutes or more, double up to make groups of eight.

2. In each group, pause a moment and think over how you would finish this statement: *The thing in my life that gives me the most satisfaction at the moment is . . . because. . . .* Then, go around your group and let everyone explain what came to mind.

For instance, one person might say, *My children, because they give me a sense of fulfillment.* Another person might say, *Working at the hospital as a volunteer, because I get a sense of joy in helping others.* Another person might say in all honesty, *Making money gives me the greatest satisfaction, because. . . .*

3. If there is time left over, go around a second time so that everyone can finish this sentence, *The thing that I long for in my life at the moment is . . . because. . . .*

Note: Decide what you want to do at the next session — whether to take Lab 2 or move into the Spiritual Encounter track — and who is to be the leader.

What Makes Me Tick

Purpose: To help you evaluate your life from the standpoint of your own sense of accomplishment and discover the underlying drives in your life.

Setting: An informal atmosphere, with people sitting on the floor or on chairs that can be moved close together.

Time: 45 to 60 minutes, with a free period at the close for groups who want to continue a little longer. If you are able to give 90 minutes to this session, you may be able to include Spiritual Encounter 2 (see page 40).

Materials required: A workbook and pencil for everyone.

Leadership: The role of leader should rotate within the class to a different person for each session. He should be assigned the week before so that he will be prepared to explain the

procedure in his own words, model examples from his own life and collect any materials needed.

PROCEDURE

The session is divided into two parts: (1) preliminary inventory — with each person completing the Personal Achievement Inventory, page 34, in silence, (2) small-group interaction — with everyone belonging to a group of four. The groups of four can be formed at the beginning of the session or at the time for the sharing.

Time limits are suggested to help in planning the session. If you do not have time to share all of the material, it is okay.

Preliminary inventory (10 minutes)

You will look back over your life and identify specific achievements and experiences that brought you a sense of accomplishment or personal satisfaction. Then you will analyze each one for the underlying cause.

1. Turn to page 34. Here you will find an outline of three age periods: (a) ages 7 to 12, (b) ages 13 to 17, and (c) ages 18 and over.

2. In the left column, without talking to anyone, jot down three achievements for each of the periods. (The easiest way to start is to close your eyes and let your imagination take you back to your pre-teen years. Ask yourself the question, *What gave me a sense of personal achievement, accomplishment or success during this period?* You might put down: (a) *hop-scotch champion in my block,* (b) *champion marble player,* (c) *won the school spelling contest.*

3. In the right column, jot down in a word or two the reason why each accomplishment was important to you.

The reason why winning the hop-scotch championship was important might have been: *It brought recognition.* And for the marble championship, *It gave me recognition* — and the same for the school spelling contest. From this, it is possible to conclude that your lifestyle during this period was built around a "drive for recognition."

Small-group interaction (30 minutes)

1. Get together in groups of four (preferably with the same people you were with in the last session) and arrange your chairs as close together as possible.

2. Each person in turn shares with his group what he jotted down in the first category and explains why.

3. Repeat the same procedure for the second and third categories.

4. If there is time left over in your group, go around again, each person sharing the thing he considers the most rewarding experience or the greatest success in his life and why.

Note: Assign someone to be the leader for the next session and decide whether you want to take another Lab or move over to the Spiritual Encounters in Track Two.

My Family Portrait

Purpose: To help you evaluate your present family relationships and share your insights with others in a small group.

Setting: An informal atmosphere, with people sitting in groups of four, preferably with the same persons as at the previous session.

Time: 45 to 60 minutes, with a free period at the close for groups who want to continue a little longer. If you are able to give 90 minutes to this session, you may be able to include Spiritual Encounter 3 (see page 45).

Materials required: A workbook

for everyone, plus a box of crayons (broken pieces will do) for each small group.

Leadership: The role of leader should rotate within the class to a different person for each session. He should be assigned the week before so that he will be prepared to explain the procedure in his own words, model examples from his own life and collect any materials needed.

PROCEDURE

The session is divided into two parts: (1) preliminary drawing — with everyone working on his own, (2) small-group interaction — with everyone belonging to a group of four. (3) group-evaluation drawing (optional) — in the same groups of four. Time limits are suggested to help in planning the session.

Preliminary drawing (10 minutes)

Here you can think through your present family relationships and create a simple drawing or diagram to show the members of your family and the way you feel about them.

1. On page 24, draw the shape of the table where you eat most of your meals with your family. For instance, if the table where you eat most of your meals is round, draw a *circle*. If the table is rectangular, draw a *rectangle*.

2. Around the table, draw each member of the family in his place. For each person use a different color, one that indicates how you feel about the person's personality. For instance, if you feel your mother is warm and outgoing, you might select a *yellow-gold* to symbolize her. If your older brother is strong and athletic, you may want to color him *dark blue*.

3. Apart from the table draw any other people or pets that play meaningful roles in your family at the moment, such as a grandmother, a dog, an uncle, etc. Also, show the significant people missing from your family circle, such as a brother who was killed, a parent who is divorced, etc.

4. Finally, color the table to symbolize the present atmosphere in your home. If your home life is warm and very accepting, you might color the table *orange*. If you have an opposite relationship with some in the family, you may color the table both *orange* and *grey*.

Small-group interaction (30 minutes)

You will get to know each other in depth through everyone's explanation of the significant relationships in his family.

1. Sit close together in groups of four.

2. Each person in turn explains his drawing in detail to his group. Include in your explanation the why for the colors chosen.

3. If there is time left over, close your eyes for a moment and think about the thing you would like to change or improve in your family lifestyle, and why. Then go around the group, everyone explaining what came to mind.

    For instance, one person might say, *I would like to see us spend more time together as a family, because we really don't know each other.* Another person might say, *I would like to think that my dad could accept me as I am, because I want to be able to talk with him.*

Group-evaluation drawing (optional)

If you have time to evaluate your group, fine.

1. Turn to page 60, draw a circle and then your small group, symbolizing each person with a color. Then fill in the circle with a color or colors to show the different relationships within your group and how *you* fit into the group.

2. After a few minutes each person can explain his drawing to the group.

RELATIONAL LAB FOUR

A Fantasy Trip

Purpose: To enable you to discover and evaluate the value and priority systems in your present lifestyle.

Setting: An informal, casual atmosphere, with people sitting with the same persons as at the previous session.

Time: 45 to 60 minutes, with a free period after the session for groups who want to continue a little longer.

Materials required: A workbook and pencil for everyone.

Leadership: The role of leader should rotate within the class to a different person for each session. He should be assigned the week before so that he will be prepared to explain the procedure in his own words, model the steps by giving examples from his own life and collect any materials needed.

PROCEDURE

The session is divided into three parts: (1) preliminary exercise — with everyone working on his own, (2) small-group interaction — in groups of four, (3) consensus building (optional) — with each group reporting to the class as a whole.

    Time limits are recommended for

each part to help in planning the session.

Preliminary exercise (10 minutes)

You will analyze your values by choosing items that you feel would be indispensable for your own personal lifestyle.

1. Close your eyes and imagine yourself packing for a trip to an uncivilized continent to start life over. Think of ten things you would want to take with you.

2. Turn to page 71 and jot down what came to mind. For instance, you might list: *a stack of books, my guitar, a text book on organic gardening, a motorcycle with solar-powered engine, my scrapbook, golf clubs, my dog,* etc. You are free to use a little literary license and put down things that are impractical in a primitive society.

3. Now, the load must be lightened, so you can take only half the number of items. Check the five things most important to you.

Small-group interaction (20 minutes)

1. Rearrange your chairs so that you are sitting in groups of four, preferably with persons you have been with before.

2. Each person, in turn, shares the five items he would take along to start over on another continent — and explains why. The *why* will get into your whole value system.

For instance, one might say, I have chosen *my motorcycle, because I can't live without the excitement of a motorcycle; my dog, because he is a constant source of friendship; my guitar, because this is my form of leisure,* etc.

Note: The leader may want to demonstrate the sharing by explaining the five items he listed – to set the pace for openness.

Consensus building (optional)

This exercise is designed to encourage teamwork. Each small group is to agree upon the basic items for creating the new community.

1. In an open exchange the members of each group suggest items representing the lifestyle and value system they believe in.

2. One person in each small group is the corresponding secretary. He jots down the ideas of the group. Then through discussion the group decides on what they feel to be the five essentials.

3. Each corresponding secretary writes his group's list on a blackboard or posterboard for the entire class.

4. Then, as a class, compare the different reports and try to arrive at a consensus of what is felt to be the five most important things to take along in starting the new community.

Note: Since there can be strong differences of opinion, the final step could tend to be unruly and consequently self-defeating as far as building a spirit of community in the class. If the leader sees a danger of this happening, he can simply leave out the last step and close with a "celebration" song.

RELATIONAL LAB FIVE

Give a Vacation

Purpose: To share your hopes and dreams for each other by planning a fantastic vacation for the persons in your group.

Setting: Informal, with the same small groups of four that have been to-

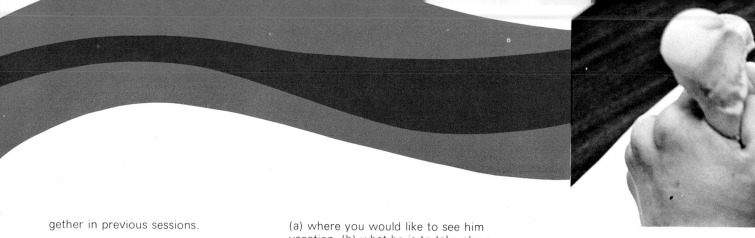

gether in previous sessions.

Time: 45 to 60 minutes, with a free period after the session for groups who want to continue a little longer.

Materials required: None.

Leadership: The role of leader should rotate within the class to a different person for each session. He should be assigned the week before so that he will be prepared to explain the procedure in his own words, model the steps by giving examples from his own life and collect any materials needed.

PROCEDURE

The session is one package. The groups of four may double up to make groups of eight if they know the others in the class well.

Vacation giving

1. Arrange the chairs (four or eight) as close together as possible in a horseshoe shape.

2. Place another chair in the horseshoe opening, facing the group.

3. Each person, in turn, sits in the empty chair at the horseshoe opening and remains quiet while the others in the group focus their attention upon him and think of the greatest vacation he could take — a vacation that would really help him in every area of his life.

4. In brainstorming fashion, proceed to bombard this person with your ideas:

(a) where you would like to see him vacation, (b) what he is to take along, (c) what he is to do, (d) what he is to think about, (e) who he is to visit, etc.

In brainstorming, each person builds on the idea suggested before hand, adding something better and better and better — until you are "blowing the mind" of each other.

For instance, one person might start out, *Betty, you have a depressing job with extreme pressure. I would like to see you vacation in the mountains — for both a summer and a winter.* Another might add, *Yes, Betty, and I would want you to go to the new ski resort areas of Australia to really get away.* And another, *When you have skied the mountains, I would want you to enjoy the wide, open plains — space — clean air.*

Or, another vacation plan might be, *Jim, you have never had a chance to know or help people outside the "big city" office. I would like to see you take about six months off to live with people of various lifestyles.* And another person might chime in at this point, *Yes, Jim, and I would like you to start out with the people in Appalachia.* And another, *While you are in Appalachia, I would like you to get acquainted with the coal miners and spend a few days working in the coal mines . . . .*

5. If there is time left over at the close, go around again and let everyone comment on the vacation that the group planned for him.

An Appreciation Party

Purpose: To express your appreciation to the others in your small group by creating for each person a symbolic gift as a token of the deeper feelings you have for him.

Setting: Casual — and ready for an "instant party."

Time: 45 to 60 minutes, with a free period at the close for the party.

Materials required: A wad of Play-Doh about the size of a golf ball for each person in the class. (A large can of Play-Doh, which costs about $1.00, will be enough for 15 or 20 people.)

Refreshments — Coke, coffee, pretzels or pizza. . . .

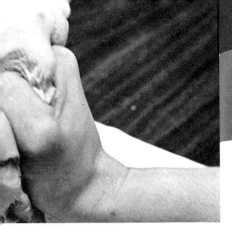

Leadership: The role of leader should rotate within the class to a different person for each session. He should be assigned the week before so that he will be prepared to explain the procedure in his own words, model the steps by giving examples from his own life and collect any materials needed.

PROCEDURE

The session is divided into three parts: (1) preliminary exercise — with everyone working on his own, (2) small-group interaction — in groups of four, (3) instant party (optional) — with all of the groups together.

Preliminary exercise (10 minutes)

You will create a series of gifts or souvenirs out of Play-Doh — one gift for each person in your small group.

1. Get together in the same groups of four that you have been in through most of the course.

2. Think specifically about the people in your group: your own personal feelings toward each of them, the times you have spent together in the course, the hopes and dreams each has expressed, and what each one of them means to you.

3. Then, with the wad of Play-Doh, sculpture tokens which symbolize your appreciation for each person in the group. The gift can represent what the person has meant to you, a souvenir of your time together, or a quality of lifestyle that you would like to give him. They do not have to be elaborate, but they should grow out of the deep personal insight you have gained of the person's inner needs and your own inner feelings for the person. For instance, a tiny doll or tricycle could symbolize the beauty of childlikeness. A spark plug could symbolize the need for someone to be a "self-starter." A ring could symbolize a deep caring.

Note: The leader may prepare Play-Doh gifts in advance to show the class what he would give to one or two people in the class. His genuineness will set the pace for the rest of the class.

Small-group interaction (30 minutes)

This part of the session is designed to let you put into words the deep personal feelings that you have for each other.

1. Each person, in turn, passes out his gifts explaining in great detail what they mean and why he chose each one.

For instance, *John, I made this door key for you. It means two things. First, it is a key into my own life that you have unlocked during this course. Second, it is a key into the future that I want you to have from me. I don't know what the future holds for you . . . but I want you to know that I want to stay in touch with you.*

2. If there is time left over, go around a second time, each person responding to the gifts that he has been given by explaining what they mean to him. For instance, John might say, *I want to thank you for the door key and say that your friendship means a lot to me . . . etc.*

3. Don't hurry this part of the session. Let it be an occasion of deep and personal sharing.

Instant party (optional)

The entire class can get together at the close for a time of general celebration and "reporting in."

1. Quickly, divide the class into two working teams: one to get the room in order and the other to prepare the refreshments. The chairs should be brought into a huge circle or stacked out of the way so that everyone can sit on the floor. Turn the lights down or light a fire — do something to create a cozy atmosphere.

2. Serve the refreshments to the class.

3. Anyone who likes, can share with the class what he got out of the course (perhaps something he discovered about himself or other people) or what the high-point of the course was for him.

Note: The leader may want to be the first to say something — and set the pace.

4. At the close, join together in a huge circle of love and celebrate your experience together by singing an appropriate song.

Personal Achievement Analysis

FEELING OF ACCOMPLISHMENT	WHY
Ages 7-12	
Ages 13-18	
Ages 18 and over	

Spiritual Encounters

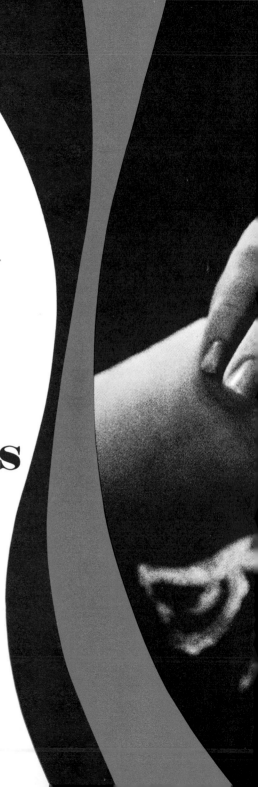

Happy are those who know they are spiritually poor:
  the Kingdom of heaven belongs to them!

Happy are those who mourn:
  God will comfort them!

Happy are the meek:
  they will receive what God has promised!

Happy are those whose greatest desire is to do what God requires:
  God will satisfy them fully!

Happy are those who show mercy to others:
  God will show mercy to them!

Happy are the pure in heart:
  they will see God!

Happy are those who work for peace among men:
  God will call them his sons!

Happy are those who suffer persecution because they do what God requires:
  the Kingdom of heaven belongs to them!

MATTHEW 5 : 3 - 10 GNFMM

Evaluating My Attitudes

SPIRITUAL ENCOUNTER ONE

Purpose: To enable you to evaluate your attitudes about your present circumstances in the light of Scripture and share your results with a small group.

Setting: A casual, informal atmosphere, with people sitting on the floor or in chairs that can be moved closely together.

Time: 45 to 60 minutes, with a free

"Happy are those who. . . ."

period following for groups who want to continue a little longer.

Materials required: A workbook and pencil for everyone.

Leadership: The role of leader should rotate within the class to a different person each session. He should be assigned the week before so that he can be prepared to explain the instructions in his own words.

The instructions for all six of the Spiritual Encounters — Track Two — are the same. If the class decides to switch tracks and go on to one of the Relational Labs or Enabling Sessions, the leader will need to become acquainted with the particular steps of the one chosen.

PROCEDURE

The session is divided into three parts: (1) preliminary exercise — with each person working on his own, (2) small-group interaction — with everyone belonging to a group of four, (3) celebration — with each small group remaining the same or combining with another to make a group of eight.

Preliminary exercise (10 minutes)

You will reflect over your life in view of the teachings of Jesus in the Sermon on the Mount.

1. The Scripture passage on page 36 (also known as the Beatitudes) deals with the radical lifestyle of the followers of Jesus as far as their attitude or outlook on life is concerned. Read it slowly, pausing along the way to think about the meaning of each phrase for your own situation.

2. When you are through, look at page 39 and fill out the Reflection Questionnaire. Phase One deals with the Scripture passage. Phase Two deals with you. The Questionnaire is not a test of skill. There is no right or wrong and no grade at the close. It is simply a tool to focus your thoughts.

Small-group interaction (15 minutes)

1. Move into groups of four persons each, preferably with others whom you do not know very well.

Note: For a feeling of "community" it is important that each small group sit close together.

2. To get started, everyone, in turn, shares what he circled for the first point in Phase One of the Questionnaire and explains why. The *why* will force you to deal with the reason behind the response — which is more important than the response itself.

3. Then everyone shares his thinking on the second point, etc., until you have gone through all of Phase One.

Celebration (20 to 30 minutes)

The object of this part of the session is to celebrate life together. In a word, to "be" a real Christian Community — caring, sharing, bearing up each other in love, trust and acceptance.

1. Pause a few minutes to allow those who did not finish Phase Two of the Questionnaire to do so.

2. Depending upon the time schedule, you can decide to stay in groups of four or move into groups of eight. If you have only 20 minutes left, stay in groups of four. If you have 30 minutes or more, move into groups of eight.

3. Each person, in turn, explains how he would complete the first point in Phase Two. Then everyone explains the second point, etc., until the exercise is completed. Here is the heart of the session. Up to this point, everything has been theory. Now, it is for real.

Note: The leader may want to share his own responses to Phase Two with the entire class. This will set the pace for honesty and openness.

4. At the close, join together in a circle of love and celebrate your experience together in either song, word or prayer. (If there are several small groups meeting, each group should dismiss itself quietly and slip out without disturbing the others.)

P.S. Don't forget to appoint a leader for the next session.

Phase One

1. My first impression when I read the Scripture passage was (circle one):

   a. ho-hum

   b. ouch

   c. wow

   d. right on

   e. whoopee

2. The word "happy" in this passage might be defined by the words (circle one):

   a. good fortune brought about through chance circumstances; lucky

   b. inner peace in the midst of painful or annoying experiences

   c. joy that springs from an inner possession

   d. contentment that comes from prior knowledge

   e. gratification of inner desires; pleasure; bliss

3. Of the eight Beatitudes, the areas where I am strongest (mark with a plus) **and the areas where I am weakest** (mark with a minus) **are:**

_____ spiritually poor (to admit that you have needs, to be open to change, to realize that you don't have it all)

_____ mourn (to feel for the hurt of others, to empathize with others because you know what it means — you have been there)

_____ meek (to enable others to be themselves, to open up, to be quiet enough to hear others)

_____ spiritual hunger (to have your priorities in spiritual perspective, to have spiritual goals and motivations)

_____ show mercy (to have compassion without conditions, sensitive and responsive, freely, unconditionally giving yourself)

_____ pure in heart (to be in touch with your inner self, unencumbered by false images, honest with yourself, God and others)

_____ peacemaker (to bridge differences without destroying others' uniquenesses, to harmonize, to bring togetherness)

_____ endurance (to be able to accept hostility and anger without fighting back, to act rather than react in circumstances)

Phase Two

1. From what I have observed of the others in my group, I would say that the Beatitude in which each person is strongest is (jot the name of each person in your group underneath the trait he has manifested):

spiritually poor

_____

mourn

_____

meek

_____

spiritual hunger

_____

show mercy

_____

pure in heart

_____

peacemaker

_____

endurance

_____

2. I would like those in my group to help me in my life to (finish the sentence):

You are like salt for all mankind. But if salt loses its taste, there is no way to make it salty again. It has become worthless; so it is thrown away and people walk on it.

You are like the light for the world. A city built on a hill cannot be hidden. Nobody lights a lamp to put it under a bowl; instead he puts it on the lamp-stand, where it gives light for everyone in the house. In the same way your light must shine before people, so that they will see the good things you do and give praise to your Father in heaven.

MATTHEW 5 : 13 -16 GNFMM

Evaluating My Objectives

SPIRITUAL ENCOUNTER TWO

Purpose: To enable you to evaluate your hopes and aspirations in the light of Scripture and share your results with a small group.

Setting: A casual, informal atmosphere, with people sitting on the floor or in chairs that can be moved closely together.

Time: 45 to 60 minutes, with a free

"You are like salt for all mankind."

41

period following for groups who want to continue a little longer.

Materials required: A workbook and pencil for everyone.

Leadership: The role of leader should rotate within the class to a different person each session. He should be assigned the week before so that he can be prepared to explain the instructions in his own words.

The instructions for all six of the Spiritual Encounters — Track Two — are the same. If the class decides to switch tracks and go on to one of the Relational Labs or Enabling Sessions, the leader will need to become acquainted with the particular steps of the one chosen.

PROCEDURE

The session is divided into three parts: (1) preliminary exercise — with each person working on his own, (2) small-group interaction — with everyone belonging to a group of four, (3) celebration — with each small group remaining the same or combining with another to make a group of eight.

Preliminary exercise (10 minutes)

You will reflect over your life in view of the teachings of Jesus in the Sermon on the Mount.

1. The Scripture passage on page 40 describes the role of the Christian in in the world as being like salt and light. The chances are that you have never stopped to consider the implications for your lifestyle. Here is the challenge of this session. Read the passage slowly, pausing along the way to let the Holy Spirit speak to you.

2. When you are through, look at page 43 and fill out the Reflection Questionnaire. Phase One deals with the Scripture passage. Phase Two deals with you. The Questionnaire is not a test of skill. There is no right or wrong and no grade at the close. It is simply a tool to focus your thoughts.

Small-group interaction (15 minutes)

1. Move into groups of four persons each, preferably with others whom you do not know very well.

Note: For a feeling of "community" it is important that each small group sit close together.

2. To get started, everyone, in turn, shares what he circled for the first point in Phase One of the Questionnaire and explains why. The *why* will force you to deal with the reason behind the response — which is more important than the response itself.

3. Then everyone shares his thinking on the second point, etc., until you have gone through all of Phase One.

Celebration (20 to 30 minutes)

The object of this part of the session is to celebrate life together. In a word, to "be" a real Christian Community — caring, sharing, bearing up each other in love, trust and acceptance.

1. Pause a few minutes to allow those who did not finish Phase Two of the Questionnaire to do so.

2. Depending upon the time schedule, you can decide to stay in groups of four or move into groups of eight. If you have only 20 minutes left, stay in groups of four. If you have 30 minutes or more, move into groups of eight.

3. Each person, in turn, explains how he would complete the first point in Phase Two. Then everyone explains the second point, etc., until the exercise is completed. Here is the heart of the session. Up to this point, everything has been theory. Now, it is for real.

Note: The leader may want to share his own responses to Phase Two with the entire class. This will set the pace for honesty and openness.

4. At the close, join together in a circle of love and celebrate your experience together in either song, word or prayer. (If there are several small groups meeting, each group should dismiss itself quietly and slip out without disturbing the others.)

P.S. Don't forget to appoint a leader for the next session.

Phase One

1. The thought of being "salt for all mankind" and "the light for all the world" is something that *(circle one):*

    a. leaves me cold

    b. frightens me

    c. grabs me

    d. blows my mind

2. According to this passage, the Christian community should be a force in history by their *(rank 1 to 4 in order of importance):*

____individual purity

____radical lifestyle of love

____involvement in the needs of society

____separation from society

3. In my estimation, the reason why the Christian community I am a part of is not a force in society is that we don't intimately know *(circle one):*

    a. God

    b. each other

    c. the Scriptures

    d. the needs of society

4. I find the quotation by Robert Raines on page 15 *(circle one):*

    a. right on target

    b. off base a little

    c. way out in left field

Phase Two

1. My present objectives in life are:

2. The person or experience that has had the greatest influence in shaping my present thinking is:

3. What brings me the greatest personal satisfaction is:

You have heard that men were told in the past, "Do not murder; anyone who commits murder will be brought before the judge." But now I tell you: whoever is angry with his brother will be brought before the judge; whoever calls his brother 'You good-for-nothing!' will be brought before the Council; and whoever calls his brother a worthless fool will be in danger of going to the fire of hell. So if you are about to offer your gift to God at the altar and there you remember that your brother has something against you, leave your gift there in front of the altar and go at once to make peace with your brother; then come back and offer your gift to God.

MATTHEW 5 : 21 -24 GNFMM

Evaluating My Relationships

SPIRITUAL ENCOUNTER THREE

Purpose: To enable you to evaluate your present relationships in the light of Scripture and share your results with a small group.

Setting: A casual, informal atmosphere, with people sitting on the floor or in chairs that can be moved close together.

Time: 45 to 60 minutes, with a free

" . . . whoever calls his brother 'You good for nothing'. . . . "

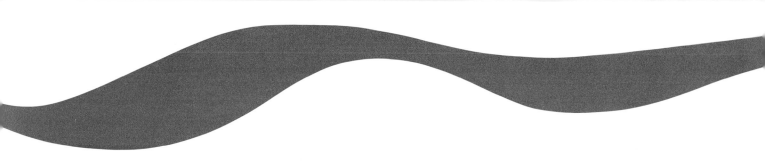

period following for groups who want to continue a little longer.

Materials required: A workbook and pencil for everyone.

Leadership: The role of leader should rotate within the class to a different person each session. He should be assigned the week before so that he can be prepared to explain the instructions in his own words.

The instructions for all six of the Spiritual Encounters — Track Two — are the same. If the class decides to switch tracks and go on to one of the Relational Labs or Enabling Sessions, the leader will need to become acquainted with the particular steps of the one chosen.

PROCEDURE

The session is divided into three parts: (1) preliminary exercise — with each person working on his own, (2) small-group interaction — with everyone belonging to a group of four, (3) celebration — with each small group remaining the same or combining with another to make a group of eight.

Preliminary exercise (10 minutes)

You will reflect over your life in view of the teachings of Jesus in the Sermon on the Mount.

1. The Scripture passage on page 44 sets forth for the followers of Jesus a whole new basis for dealing with interpersonal relationships, conflicts and hostilities. Read the passage slowly, pausing along the way to think about the meaning of the words for your life.

2. When you are through, look at page 47 and fill out the Reflection Questionnaire. Phase One deals with the Scripture passage. Phase Two deals with you. The Questionnaire is not a test of skill. There is no right or wrong and no grade at the close. It is simply a tool to focus your thoughts.

Small-group interaction (15 minutes)

1. Move into groups of four persons each, preferably with others whom you do not know very well.

Note: For a feeling of "community" it is important that each small group sit close together.

2. To get started, everyone, in turn, shares what he circled for the first point in Phase One of the Questionnaire and explains why. The *why* will force you to deal with the reason behind the response — which is more important than the response itself.

3. Then everyone shares his thinking on the second point, etc., until you have gone through all of Phase One.

Celebration (20 to 30 minutes)

The object of this part of the session is to celebrate life together. In a word, to "be" a real Christian Community — caring, sharing, bearing up each other in love, trust and acceptance.

1. Pause a few minutes to allow those who did not finish Phase Two of the Questionnaire to do so.

2. Depending upon the time schedule, you can decide to stay in groups of four or move into groups of eight. If you have only 20 minutes left, stay in groups of four. If you have 30 minutes or more, move into groups of eight.

3. Each person, in turn, explains how he would complete the first point in Phase Two. Then everyone explains the second point, etc., until the exercise is completed. Here is the heart of the session. Up to this point, everything has been theory. Now, it is for real.

Note: The leader may want to share his own responses to Phase Two with the entire class. This will set the pace for honesty and openness.

4. At the close, join together in a circle of love and celebrate your experience together in either song, word or prayer. (If there are several small groups meeting, each group should dismiss itself quietly and slip out without disturbing the others.)

P.S. Don't forget to appoint a leader for the next session.

Phase One

1. **Murder is defined in the Scripture passage as** *(circle one):*

   a. killing your brother

   b. slandering your brother to others

   c. tearing down your brother's self worth

   d. making it difficult for your brother

   e. not giving in to your brother

2. **According to the passage, God expects** *(circle one):*

   a. the person who has done wrong to go to God and make it right

   b. the person who has been wronged to go to God and make it right

   c. the person who has done wrong to go to the person and make it right

   d. the person who has been wronged to go to the person and make it right

3. **Jot down in the space below the names of the people with whom you live at the moment. Then, beside each name, place one of the following symbols:**

○ Our relationship is completely affirming. I build up this person and he builds me up. We enable each other to be our best selves.

◐ Our relationship is half-affirming. I try to build up this person but he refuses to build me up.

◑ Our relationship is half-affirming in the other direction. This person tries to build me up, but I do not know how to build him up.

● Our relationship is mutually destructive. I tear down this person's self-worth and he tears down my self-worth. We are destroying each other.

———————————————
———————————————
———————————————
———————————————
———————————————
———————————————

Phase Two

1. **Since starting in this small group, I think I have started** *(circle one):*

   a. to believe in my own unique worth and special gifts

   b. to accept some of my own weaknesses and faults

   c. to trust God for my problems

   d. to celebrate life in a new way

   e. none of these

   f. all of these

2. **The kind of person that helps me to come out of my shell and be myself is** *(list three adjectives):*

3. **The area in my life where I have made the least progress lately is** *(finish the sentence):*

THE OTHER SEX

You have heard that it was said, 'Do not commit adultery.' But now I tell you: anyone who looks at a woman and wants to possess her is guilty of committing adultery with her in his heart. So if your right eye causes you to sin, take it out and throw it away! It is much better for you to lose a part of your body than to have your whole body thrown into hell.

MATTHEW 5 : 27 -29 GNFMM

THE OTHER CHEEK

You have heard that it was said, 'An eye for an eye, and a tooth for a tooth.' But now I tell you: do not take revenge on someone who does you wrong. If anyone slaps you on the right cheek, let him slap you on the left cheek too.

MATTHEW 5 : 38 -39 GNFMM

THE OTHER SIDE

You have heard that it was said, 'Love your friends and hate your enemies.' But now I tell you: love your enemies, and pray for those who mistreat you, so that you will become the sons of your Father in heaven.

MATTHEW 5 : 43 -45 GNFMM

Evaluating My Ethics

SPIRITUAL ENCOUNTER FOUR

Purpose: To enable you to evaluate your ethics in three areas of your life: (a) the other sex, (b) the other cheek, (c) the other side.

Setting: A casual, informal atmos-phere, with people sitting on the floor or in chairs that can be moved closely together.

Time: 45 to 60 minutes, with a free period following for groups who want to continue a little longer.

Materials required: A workbook and

"You have heard . . . but I say. . . ."

pencil for everyone.

Leadership: The role of leader should rotate within the class to a different person each session. He should be assigned the week before so that he can be prepared to explain the instructions in his own words.

The instructions for all six of the Spiritual Encounters — Track Two — are the same. If the class decides to switch tracks and go on to one of the Relational Labs or Enabling Sessions, the leader will need to become acquainted with the particular steps of the one chosen.

PROCEDURE

The session is divided into three parts: (1) preliminary exercise — with each person working on his own, (2) small-group interaction — with everyone belonging to a group of four, (3) celebration — with each small group remaining the same or combining with another to make a group of eight.

Preliminary exercise (10 minutes)

You will reflect over your life in view of the teachings of Jesus in the Sermon on the Mount.

1. The Scripture passages on page 48 spell out a new system of morality for the followers of Jesus. In three different instances, Jesus redefines the Old Testament standards of behavior. These three statements are among the hardest to understand of Jesus' teachings. They are also three of the most timely for today. Read the passage slowly, pausing along the way to think about the meaning of the words for your life.

2. When you are through, look at page 51 and fill out the Reflection Questionnaire. Phase One deals with the Scripture passage. Phase Two deals with you. The Questionnaire is not a test of skill. There is no right or wrong and no grade at the close. It is simply a tool to focus your thoughts.

Small-group interaction (15 minutes)

1. Move into groups of four persons each, preferably with others whom you do not know very well.

Note: For a feeling of "community" it is important that each small group sit close together.

2. To get started, everyone, in turn, shares what he circled for the first point in Phase One of the Questionnaire and explains why. The *why* will force you to deal with the reason behind the response — which is more important than the response itself.

3. Then everyone shares his thinking on the second point, etc., until you have gone through all of Phase One.

Celebration (20 to 30 minutes)

The object of this part of the session is to celebrate life together. In a word, to "be" a real Christian Community — caring, sharing, bearing up each other in love, trust and acceptance.

1. Pause a few minutes to allow those who did not finish Phase Two of the Questionnaire to do so.

2. Depending upon the time schedule, you can decide to stay in groups of four or move into groups of eight. If you have only 20 minutes left, stay in groups of four. If you have 30 minutes or more, move into groups of eight.

3. Each person, in turn, explains how he would complete the first point in Phase Two. Then everyone explains the second point, etc., until the exercise is completed. Here is the heart of the session. Up to this point, everything has been theory. Now, it is for real.

Note: The leader may want to share his own responses to Phase Two with the entire class. This will set the pace for honesty and openness.

4. At the close, join together in a circle of love and celebrate your experience together in either song, word or prayer. (If there are several small groups meeting, each group should dismiss itself quietly and slip out without disturbing the others.)

P.S. Don't forget to appoint a leader for the next session.

Phase One

1. The common thread that runs through all three paragraphs is *(circle one)*:

   a. a new measurement for judging Christian behavior

   b. a radical new pattern for developing a Christian lifestyle

   c. a new focus for forming Christian relationships

2. The difference in the concept of love as portrayed by Jesus and the one portrayed by Hollywood is *(circle one)*:

   a. one is all giving, the other is all getting

   b. one is enabling persons, the other is disabling them

   c. one sees others as persons, the other sees people as things

   d. one is costly in terms of commitment, the other is not

3. When I think of the sexual act, I think of *(rank 1 to 3 in order of significance)*:

   ____ physical pleasure

   ____ a personal relationship

   ____ a lifetime commitment

4. In my opinion, the best way to deal with lust is *(circle one)*:

   a. repress it (deny it)

   b. suppress it (force it under)

   c. confess it (admit it)

   d. overcome it (fight it)

   e. rechannel it (sublimate it)

   f. express it (do it)

Phase Two

1. Of the three paragraphs in the Scripture passage, the hardest one for me is to live is *(rank 1 to 3 in order of difficulty)*:

   ____ the other sex

   ____ the other cheek

   ____ the other side

2. If I am going to do something about the area that is causing me the greatest problem, I must start out by *(finish the sentence)*:

No one can be a slave to two masters: he will hate one and love the other; he will be loyal to one and despise the other. You cannot serve both God and money.

This is why I tell you: do not be worried about the food and drink you need to stay alive, or about clothes for your body. After all, isn't life worth more than food? and isn't the body worth more than clothes? Look at the birds flying around: they do not plant seeds, gather a harvest, and put it into barns; your Father in heaven takes care of them! Aren't you worth much more than birds? Which one of you can live a few years more by worrying about it?

And why worry about clothes? Look how the wild flowers grow: they do not work or make clothes for themselves. But I tell you that not even Solomon, as rich as he was, had clothes as beautiful as one of these flowers. It is God who clothes the wild grass — grass that is here today, gone tomorrow, burned up in the oven. Will he not be all the more sure to clothe you? How little is your faith! So do not start worrying: "Where will my food come from? or my drink? or my clothes?" (These are the things the heathen are always after.) Your Father in heaven knows that you need all these things. Instead, give first place to his Kingdom and to what he requires, and he will provide you with all these other things. So do not worry about tomorrow; it will have enough worries of its own. There is no need to add to the troubles each day brings.

MATTHEW 6 : 24 -34 GNFMM

"No one can be a slave of two masters"

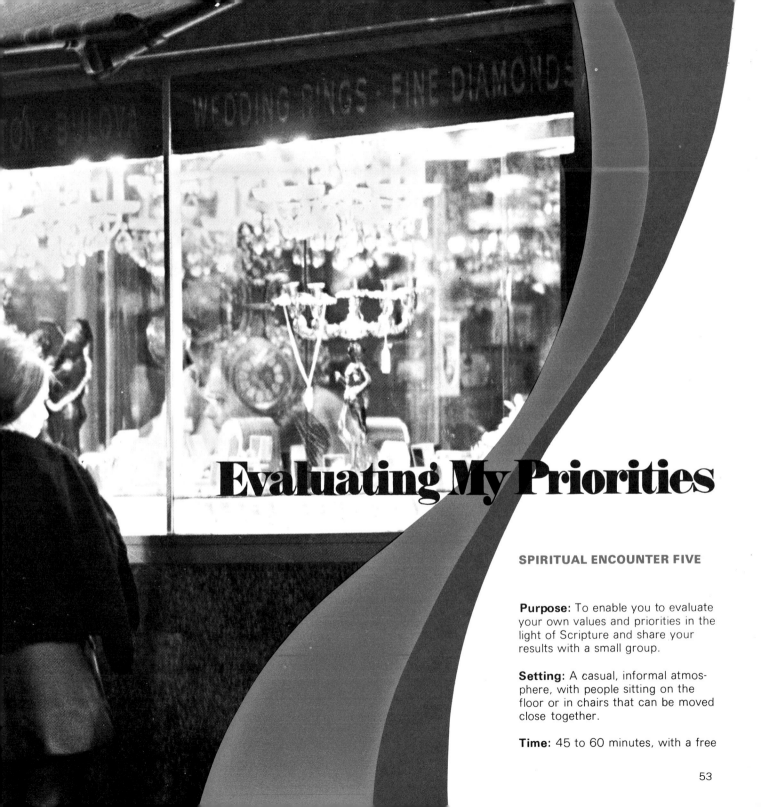

Evaluating My Priorities

SPIRITUAL ENCOUNTER FIVE

Purpose: To enable you to evaluate your own values and priorities in the light of Scripture and share your results with a small group.

Setting: A casual, informal atmosphere, with people sitting on the floor or in chairs that can be moved close together.

Time: 45 to 60 minutes, with a free

period following for groups who want to continue a little longer.

Materials required: A workbook and pencil for everyone.

Leadership: The role of leader should rotate within the class to a different person each session. He should be assigned the week before so that he can be prepared to explain the instructions in his own words.

The instructions for all six of the Spiritual Encounters — Track Two — are the same. If the class decides to switch tracks and go on to one of the Relational Labs or Enabling Sessions, the leader will need to become acquainted with the particular steps of the one chosen.

PROCEDURE

The session is divided into three parts: (1) preliminary exercise — with each person working on his own, (2) small-group interaction — with everyone belonging to a group of four, (3) celebration — with each small group remaining the same or combining with another to make a group of eight.

Preliminary exercise (10 minutes)

You will reflect over your life in view of the teachings of Jesus in the Sermon on the Mount:

1. The Scripture passage on page 52 is one of those disturbing passages in the Bible that causes a lot of people to shake their heads. It suggests a lifestyle for the followers of Jesus that is radically different from what is often taught today. Read the passage slowly, pausing along the way to think about the meaning for your life.

2. When you are through, look at page 55 and fill out the Reflection Questionnaire. Phase One deals with the Scripture passage. Phase Two deals with you. The Questionnaire is not a test of skill. There is no right or wrong and no grade at the close. It is simply a tool to focus your thoughts.

Small-group interaction (15 minutes)

1. Move into groups of four persons each, preferably with others whom you do not know very well.

Note: For a feeling of "community" it is important that each small group sit close together.

2. To get started, everyone, in turn, shares what he circled for the first point in Phase One of the Questionnaire and explains why. The *why* will force you to deal with the reason behind the response — which is more important than the response itself.

3. Then everyone shares his thinking on the second point, etc., until you have gone through all of Phase One.

Celebration (20 to 30 minutes)

The object of this part of the session is to celebrate life together. In a word, to "be" a real Christian Community — caring, sharing, bearing up each other in love, trust and acceptance.

1. Pause a few minutes to allow those who did not finish Phase Two of the Questionnaire to do so.

2. Depending upon the time schedule, you can decide to stay in groups of four or move into groups of eight. If you have only 20 minutes left, stay in groups of four. If you have 30 minutes or more, move into groups of eight.

3. Each person, in turn, explains how he would complete the first point in Phase Two. Then everyone explains the second point, etc., until the exercise is completed. Here is the heart of the session. Up to this point, everything has been theory. Now, it is for real.

Note: The leader may want to share his own responses to Phase Two with the entire class. This will set the pace for honesty and openness.

4. At the close, join together in a circle of love and celebrate your experience together in either song, word or prayer. (If there are several small groups meeting, each group should dismiss itself quietly and slip out without disturbing the others.)

P.S. Don't forget to appoint a leader for the next session.

Phase One

1. The first thing that struck me when I read this passage was *(circle one):*

   a. I am trying to serve two masters, and it doesn't work

   b. my worry is a sign that I have my values all messed up

   c. I shouldn't worry about the future

   d. I put too much importance on things

   e. none of these

   f. all of these

2. In all honesty, the thing that I want most out of life at the moment is to *(rank 1, 2, 3, etc., in order of priority):*

_____ have lots of friends

_____ have plenty of money

_____ have a personal relationship with God

_____ develop my creative potential (physical or mental) to the fullest

_____ discover real inner peace of mind

_____ find success in my chosen field

_____ make a contribution to mankind in some way

_____ make one person supremely happy

3. I find the quotation by Anthony T. Padovano on page 72 *(circle one):*

   a. hard to understand

   b. hard to accept

   c. hard to do

Phase Two

1. If I were to take the Scripture passage seriously, it would mean *(circle one):*

   a. a radical change in my present values

   b. a radical change in my priorities

   c. a radical change in my lifestyle

   d. no change at all

2. I want the whole will of God in my life *(circle one):*

   a. all of the time

   b. most of the time

   c. some of the time

   d. in a crisis

   e. vaguely

   f. I don't know

So then, everyone who hears these words of mine and obeys them will be like a wise man who built his house on the rock. The rain poured down, the rivers flooded over, and the winds blew hard against that house. But it did not fall, because it had been built on the rock. Everyone who hears these words of mine and does not obey them will be like a foolish man who built his house on the sand. The rain poured down, the rivers flooded over, the winds blew hard against that house, and it fell. What a terrible fall that was!
MATTHEW 7 : 24 -27 GNFMM

Evaluating My Lifestyle

SPIRITUAL ENCOUNTER SIX

Purpose: To enable you to evaluate your commitment to Jesus Christ in the light of Scripture and share your results with a few others in small groups.

Setting: A casual, informal atmosphere, with people sitting on the floor or in chairs that can be moved close together.

Time: 45 to 60 minutes, with a free period following for groups who want to continue a little longer.

"... like a
wise man
who built
his house
on the rock."

57

Materials required: A workbook and pencil for everyone.

Leadership: The role of leader should rotate within the class to a different person each session. He should be assigned the week before so that he can be prepared to explain the instructions in his own words.

The instructions for all six of the Spiritual Encounters — Track Two — are the same. If the class decides to switch tracks and go on to one of the Relational Labs or Enabling Sessions, the leader will need to become acquainted with the particular steps of the one chosen.

PROCEDURE

The session is divided into three parts: (1) preliminary exercise — with each person working on his own, (2) small-group interaction — with everyone belonging to a group of four, (3) celebration — with each small group remaining the same or combining with another to make a group of eight.

Preliminary exercise (10 minutes)

You will reflect over your life in view of the teachings of Jesus in the Sermon on the Mount.

1. The Scripture passage on page 56 describes two hypothetical builders, one who built his lifestyle on a rock and another who built his lifestyle on the sand. Jesus used this parable at the close of the Sermon on the Mount to summarize his teaching. Read the passage slowly, pausing along the way to let the Holy Spirit speak to you about your lifestyle.

2. When you are through, look at page 59 and fill out the Reflection Questionnaire. Phase One deals with the Scripture passage. Phase Two deals with you. The Questionnaire is not a test of skill. There is no right or wrong and no grade at the close. It is simply a tool to focus your thoughts.

Small-group interaction (15 minutes)

1. Move into groups of four persons each, preferably with others whom you do not know very well.

Note: For a feeling of "community" it is important that each small group sit close together.

2. To get started, everyone, in turn, shares what he circled for the first point in Phase One of the Questionnaire and explains why. The *why* will force you to deal with the reason behind the response — which is more important than the response itself.

3. Then everyone shares his thinking on the second point, etc., until you have gone through all of Phase One.

Celebration (20 to 30 minutes)

The object of this part of the session is to celebrate life together. In a word, to "be" a real Christian Community — caring, sharing, bearing up each other in love, trust and acceptance.

1. Pause a few minutes to allow those who did not finish Phase Two of the Questionnaire to do so.

2. Depending upon the time schedule, you can decide to stay in groups of four or move into groups of eight. If you have only 20 minutes left, stay in groups of four. If you have 30 minutes or more, move into groups of eight.

3. Each person, in turn, explains how he would complete the first point in Phase Two. Then everyone explains the second point, etc., until the exercise is completed. Here is the heart of the session. Up to this point, everything has been theory. Now, it is for real.

Note: The leader may want to share his own responses to Phase Two with the entire class. This will set the pace for honesty and openness.

4. At the close, join together in a circle of love and celebrate your experience together in either song, word or prayer. (If there are several small groups meeting, each group should dismiss itself quietly and slip out without disturbing the others.)

P.S. Don't forget to appoint a leader for the next session.

Phase One

1. The thing I feel Jesus was teaching in the Scripture passage is that *(circle one)*:

   a. my lifestyle is unimportant as long as it is founded on the rock

   b. the only way you can know if your lifestyle is right is to see it in a "storm"

   c. you can avoid tragedy by building soundly in the first place

   d. storms are good because they wash away lifestyles that are unsound.

2. The word "rock" in this passage refers to *(circle one)*:

   a. Jesus Christ

   b. the church

   c. the Scripture

   d. the inner life in a person

3. In my own spiritual experience, the closest I have come to going through "bad weather" like the storm described in the Scripture passage was *(finish the sentence)*:

4. The thing that sustained me through this stormy period in my life was *(finish the sentence)*:

5. I find that the statement by Sam Shoemaker on page 23 *(circle one)*:

   a. describes me exactly

   b. leaves me cold

   c. causes me to think

   d. describes my former lifestyle

Phase Two

Finish the following sentences:

1. The high point in this course for me has been:

2. The greatest thing I have learned from this course is:

3. If I knew that I could count on the support of my group, the thing I would give myself to in the future would be:

59

Enabling Sessions

instructions for the enabling sessions

Purpose: To deal with the basis for Christian lifestyle from the viewpoint of Scripture and to share the results with each other in small groups.

Setting: Informal groups of four, sitting on the floor or in chairs that can be moved close together.

Time required: A minimum of 60 minutes, plus a free period at the close for groups who need a little more time.

Materials required: A pencil and workbook for everyone.

PROCEDURE

All six sessions are divided into three parts: (1) preliminary exercise — with each person working on his own, (2) small-group interaction — with everyone belonging to a small group of four, (3) depth encounter — with everyone staying in his small group.

The leader of the class should be prepared to explain the instructions in his own words, giving examples from his paraphrase and application in order to set the pace for honesty.

Preliminary exercise (15 minutes)

1. In silence, read over the Scripture passage for the session, pausing after each verse to jot in the margin one of the following symbols:

△ If you understand the verse clearly
? If you have a question about the meaning
↑ If you get special inspiration from the verse
↓ If you really get convicted about something in your life

You can draw more than one symbol for each verse, but you must have at least one for each verse.

2. Ask yourself the question, *Which two verses speak to my need or my situation?* Underline them.

3. Then, in the top-left corner of the work sheet, write the number of the first verse you have chosen and draw a circle around it.

Read the verse again, and starting with the first part, rewrite it in your own words. (Note the sample on page 64.)

For the first part of verse 2, you might paraphrase the words: *Listen here, gang, the next time you run into difficulty and feel like 'throwing in the sponge,' remember this and let the experience stick in your mind.*

You may want to rewrite the first verse two or three times, each time going a little deeper into the meaning as you see it.

Then, go a step further and think of the verse in terms of your own situation at school, at work, at home or at church. Try to include in your paraphrase what the verse really means in the situation where you live. For instance, on the verse we

just paraphrased, you might tack on to the end of the paraphrase: *and this means the next time you get hollered at at home.*

4. When you have finished with the first verse you underlined, write the number of the second verse you underlined and put a circle around it. Then, proceed to rewrite this verse in your own words in the same way — expanding on the deeper meaning of the verse for your life and situation.

5. When 10 minutes are up, regardless of whether everyone is through with his paraphrase, move on to the application.

Ask yourself the question, *As far as these two verses are concerned, what is the thing I must work on in my life?* It can be anything from a bad attitude at work to a broken relationship with your wife, but it should be honest and specific — very specific.

Whatever comes to mind as the need in your life at the moment, jot it under the word *Application* at the bottom of your work sheet. It does not have to be long. Just a few words will do, such as *screaming at the children.*

Then, under the need put down three things you can do about it during the next week. If *screaming at the children* is the problem in your life, you might

jot down:

*Tell them I am
sorry when I scream
at them. Ask their help.
Commit the problem to God.*

After a couple of minutes, the leader
will call "time" and ask you to move
into small groups.

Small-group interaction (30 minutes)

1. Gather together in groups of four
and have one person in each group
serve as the moderator. His task is to
see that the discussion stays on the
subject and the material is covered.
The role of moderator should rotate
to a different person at each session.

2. The moderator asks each person in
his group to explain which verses he
picked for his paraphrase — and why.
(The *why* will be interesting in itself.)

Then those who have paraphrased
the first verse in the passage read
aloud what they have written. As
each paraphrase is read, the moderator
should listen
for something that
would be good for "gut level" discussion. He can then come back with
a question that focuses the discussion
on this area. For instance, *Bill, what did
you mean by "uptight"?* or, *Helen,
would you mind giving me an example
out of your own experience to clarify
what you mean?*

3. After four or five minutes move on
to the next verse that has been paraphrased and do the same.

4. Follow this procedure verse by
verse through the passage until all
of the verses that have been paraphrased have been covered — or
until the 30 minutes are up.

Depth encounter (15 minutes)

1. In the small groups each person in
turn shares his application, explaining
the thing he wants — needs — to
work on in his life and what he is
going to do about it.

2. After the sharing, gather together
and form a circle of love. In oneness
and dependence, pray specifically
for each other, using the first person,
I . . . me . . . my.

3. When your small group is through,
dismiss yourselves and slip out quietly
without disturbing the groups that
are still meeting.

ENABLING SESSION SAMPLE

Making Right My Foundation

6. *Therefore, since Jesus was delivered to you as Christ and Lord, live your lives in union with him.*

7. *Be rooted in him; be built in him; be consolidated in the faith you were taught; let your hearts overflow with thankfulness.*

8. *Be on your guard; do not let your minds be captured by hollow and delusive speculations, based on traditions of man-made teachings and centered on the elemental spirits of the universe and not on Christ.*

9. *For it is in Christ that the complete being of the Godhead dwells embodied,*

10. *and in him you have been brought to completion. Every power and authority in the universe is subject to him as Head.*

COLOSSIANS 2 : 6 -10 NEB

⑥ Inasmuch as you have committed your life to Christ — yielded the rights — given over the keys — make sure that you follow through now and stay close to Christ.

⑦ Just like a little seed, let Jesus Christ in you grow into a mature plant, until your spiritual life abounds in joy.

FOR YOUR APPLICATION

1. Using the illustration of a plant as is used in the Scripture, where would you say you are in your spiritual growth at the moment?

   just starting out as a seed

2. If you could set a goal for the next month in your spiritual growth, for what would you strive?

   to begin every day with God

3. Do you feel that the members of your small group really care about each other?

   a little bit

Making Right My Attitudes

2. My brothers, whenever you have to face trials of many kinds, count yourselves supremely happy . . .

3. . . . in the knowledge that such testing of your faith breeds fortitude,

4. and if you give fortitude full play you will go on to complete a balanced character that will fall short in nothing.

5. If any of you falls short in wisdom, he should ask God for it and it will be given him, for God is a generous giver who neither refuses nor reproaches anyone.

JAMES 1 : 2 -5 NEB

FOR YOUR APPLICATION

1. In all honesty, what is the greatest "trial" you are facing at the moment?

2. What alternatives do you have for dealing with the problem?

3. Do you feel that you can trust the others in your small group to help you in dealing with the situation?

ENABLING SESSION **2**

Making Right My Objectives

16. Let the message of Christ dwell among you in all its richness. Instruct and admonish each other with the utmost wisdom. Sing thankfully in your hearts to God, with psalms and hymns and spiritual songs.

17. Whatever you are doing, whether you speak or act, do everything in the name of the Lord Jesus, giving thanks to God the Father through him.

COLOSSIANS 3 : 16 -17 NEB

FOR YOUR APPLICATION

1. Are you as crazy about Jesus Christ today as you were when you first came to know him?

2. Do you enjoy getting together with Christians for real spiritual fellowship as much as you enjoy sports or recreation?

3. Would you be willing to belong to a fellowship where the others in the group would check up on your spiritual life and hold you accountable for your growth?

Making Right My Relationships

8. To sum up: be one in thought and feeling, all of you; be full of brotherly affection, kindly and humble-minded.

9. Do not repay wrong with wrong, or abuse with abuse; on the contrary, retaliate with blessing, for a blessing is the inheritance to which you yourselves have been called.

10. Whoever loves life and would see good days must restrain his tongue from evil and his lips from deceit;

11. (He) must turn from wrong and do good, seek peace and pursue it.

12. For the Lord's eyes are turned towards the righteous, and his ears are open to their prayers; but the Lord's face is set against wrong-doers.

1 PETER 3 : 8 -12 NEB

FOR YOUR APPLICATION

1. Which verse in the Scripture passage is going to be the hardest for you to live by?

2. Since starting this course, which area in your spiritual life has seen the greatest growth? the least growth?

3. From your observation, where has been the greatest growth in the life of the person on your right? What about the person on your left?

ENABLING SESSION 4

Making Right My Ethics

7. Make no mistake about this: God is not to be fooled; a man reaps what he sows.

8. If a man sows seed in the field of his lower nature, he will reap from it a harvest of corruption, but if he sows in the field of the Spirit, the Spirit will bring him a harvest of eternal life.

9. So let us never tire of doing good, for if we do not slacken our efforts we shall in due time reap our harvest.

10. Therefore, as opportunity offers, let us work for the good of all, especially members of the household of the faith.

GALATIANS 6 : 7 -10 NEB

FOR YOUR APPLICATION

1. When do you experience the greatest tug-of-war between your "lower nature" and your "spiritual nature"?

2. When you are struggling, do you have anyone to whom you can go for help or support?

3. Do you feel that the members of your group care enough about you that you can go to them?

FOR YOUR PARAPHRASE

Making Right My Priorities

1. Therefore, my brothers, I implore you by God's mercy to offer your very selves to him: a living sacrifice, dedicated and fit for his acceptance, the worship offered by mind and heart.

2. Adapt yourselves no longer to the pattern of this present world, but let your minds be remade and your whole nature thus transformed. Then you will be able to discern the will of God, and to know what is good, acceptable, and perfect.

ROMANS 12: 1-2 NEB

FOR YOUR APPLICATION

1. At the present moment, do you feel that you are giving as much of yourself as you know how, to all of the will of God as you understand it for your life?

2. What do you feel is going to be the next great frontier in the church?

3. Specifically, how could you and your group fit into this frontier?

ENABLING SESSION **6**

Making Right My Lifestyle

24. You know (do you not) that at the sports all the runners run the race, though only one wins the prize. Like them, run to win!
25. But every athlete goes into strict training. They do it to win a fading wreath; we, a wreath that never fades.
26. For my part, I (Paul) run with a clear goal before me; I am like a boxer who does not beat the air;
27. I bruise my own body and make it know its master, for fear that after preaching to others I should find my-self rejected.
1 CORINTHIANS 9: 24-27 NEB

FOR YOUR APPLICATION

1. Using the same analogy that Paul used in the Scripture passage, how would you compare your spiritual training discipline to Paul's?

2. What has been the greatest achievement in the course as far as your spiritual life is concerned?

3. If you had a chance to belong to another group like this, would you do it?

4. What is the greatest wish you have for each person in your group?

"Christians are inconsistent
when they maintain that
the lifestyle of Jesus was
suitable for Jesus but not
for us. We are short-
sighted when we claim we
shall accept the doctrine
of Jesus but not his be-
havior. We seldom seek
to correct the doctrine
of Jesus; we more
easily refine and excuse
his behavior. Yet Jesus
reveals less in his words
than in his lifestyle. And
he reveals not only who
God is but what a man
must become. . . ."

Anthony T. Padovano
Dawn Without Darkness

Membership
in a group
is like a
marriage bond.
It involves
a commitment
that is the
essence of
"life together."

Better look
before
you leap.

The noted author
and editor of
Faith at Work magazine
shares his own insights
concerning common fears
about small groups.

It's Worth the Risk

by Wally Howard

When Danny, a former olympic athlete, arrived for the first meeting of a small group in our home, he was so scared that he drove around the block three times before he could get up the nerve to come in. His wife refused to come at all. But when the meeting was over, Danny called his wife and said, "It's the most wonderful thing in the world. God was there, and I had goose bumps all over me."

Let's face it: real fellowship is no lemon meringue pie. It is tough, and it can be costly. C. H. Spurgeon used to define fellowship as "knowing and being known." This can be a frightening as well as a releasing experience.

If we are going to lead small groups, we should be aware of fears and how they can be overcome. Here, for observation and evaluation, are six fears which I have personally identified.

(1) *The fear of being known.* Most of us spend a good deal of time dressing up for a masquerade — to impress people, to be well thought of, to be accepted — and the prospect of unmasking is not a pleasant one. Few of us like ourselves as we are and hardly expect that others will.

This article is from the book Groups That Work, *1964, Faith at Work. Reprinted by permission.*

Most of us spend
a good deal of time
dressing up for a masquerade —
to impress people,
to be well thought of,
to be accepted —
and the prospect of
unmasking is not a pleasant one.

We are afraid that we may look foolish or ignorant. "They may ask me to pray out loud," we say. "I don't want to show how little I know about the Bible." "My religion is a very personal thing and I don't want to talk about it." These statements make up the protective armor people hide behind, but the real fear is that others will see us as we are.

The antidote? Let it be known that no one *has* to participate. Allow people the privilege of listening quietly until they themselves overcome the barriers and break the silence. Our next-door neighbor, quizzical about the cars parked outside our home each Tuesday night, asked questions and was invited to a "different kind of meeting." She came cautiously and sat through six sessions without opening her mouth. Then one night, in an irrepressible outburst, she said, "I'm amazed at your openness and honesty. I didn't know people could talk this way. You have something I don't have, but I want it."

When the fearful *do* speak, we must listen respectfully. No matter how far out or how far back they may be, they must know that what they say is appreciated, and that they themselves are respected. A group is no place for arguments. An honest question may be in order, or a challenging counterproposal, but the newcomer must know that when he speaks he himself will neither be judged nor rejected.

(2) *The fear of exploitation.* Who would not be reluctant to speak if he felt that what he said would become the subject of gossip or be used against him? It must be an unquestioned rule that what is said in the group will be kept in confidence and not go outside the room. No rule of itself will guarantee this. Only a shared sense of common need, a realization that "we are in this together," and the maturity that does not need to bolster its ego by displaying inside information about other people will guarantee a group where disclosures lead to support rather than betrayal.

(3) *The fear of disappointment.* Does the group have the maturity to help me with my problem? If I do not feel that it does, I am not likely to unburden myself. And if I do decide to gamble and begin to reveal a deep need in my life but am not taken seriously — either by being given too quick, too pat answers before they have heard me out, or by having the subject changed because it gets too close to the group's own unresolved problems — I will clam up and retreat from further disclosures.

A group must not pretend to know more than it actually does, and become "amateur psychologists," as one person has put it. We need to know our limitations, appreciate the resources of pastoral counselors and therapists, and recognize when someone needs additional help.

But any group has certain powerful resources at its disposal and it must not minimize them. An honest reaction, if expressed with consideration and respect, is always in order. So are prayer and faith in a God who can work miracles. So is loving, supporting acceptance. And so is disclosure of similar personal experiences. We may not always know how God works, or how he wants to work, but we know how he has worked with us. These are the resources that any group can bring to bear on a problem, and they can go further than we realize in solving deep human needs.

(4) *The fear of change.* If interaction within a group is serious and honest, a newcomer will quickly reach the stage where he knows that changes are required of him. Most of us are resistant to change, especially if it demands that we initiate and carry through courageous new plans of action. Self-discovery may reveal areas where "soul-surgery" is demanded — and who enjoys undergoing surgery of any kind?

But a group can support its members with positive experiences of growth and victory. Thus, if a "beginner" hears the story of how someone else came through safely, and senses how much better it is on the other side, he may be far more willing to undergo the knife. Especially so if the group also administers an anaesthetic in the form of love. I once heard a marriage counselor say, "Our task is to hold a person firmly in one hand — with love — while with the other we apply the scalpel." Growth can be painful

and costly, but grow we must, and where better than in a group that cares and understands and "holds us to our best"?

(5) *The fear of failure.* Coupled with the fear of change is the fear that having taken a new step we may fall flat on our face: And to do so in plain view of the group may be more embarrassing than not to take a step at all. "I know myself," we say. "I recognize that I won't be able to stick to a resolution. And since I don't want to do anything unless I can do it well, it's best not even to begin." Thus we rationalize.

A group may be able to move such persons off dead center by sharing the resources made available through the Holy Spirit, resources made doubly powerful in a supporting fellowship. The fearful individual must be helped

to know that when he does fail — and which of us doesn't? — He can safely share his failure with the group. He may want to hide from people when he is defeated, but this is precisely the time when he needs them most.

Besides this, each individual must be accepted as unique. He must be allowed to make his own decisions, choose his own direction and move at his own pace. He must not be made to conform, but be loved and supported even when he seems to be marking time or going in the wrong direction.

(6) *The fear of sacrifice.* The whole prospect of getting involved with other people, not only disclosing our own problems but hearing the problems of others and thereby coming under unavoidable responsibility, demands a price. Do we have the time, are we willing to take the time that is

demanded to "bear one another's burdens"?

Membership in a group for personal growth, like marriage, is a bond that we must not enter into lightly. It involves a commitment that is the essence of "life together." Better look before you leap.

But if a group shows the rewards of helping and being helped — the personal advance that comes from being roped together like mountain climbers for the ascent, and the joy of participating in the growth of others — it will shout to all the world, "Come on in; the water's fine." For this is really the only way to live. Life is involvement!

If we are faced with any of these fears, three courses of action are open to us. We can withdraw into our shells and try to "go it alone" — not letting

anyone know our struggles — and in self-sufficiency try to convince ourselves that we need no human fellowship.

Or we can withdraw into a superficial and comfortable group or one where we can be in control — into groups which offer no real challenge. Thus, we can drift along in the mediocrity and conformity which characterizes so much of modern society and the church and be just "one of the group."

But we will not find God's way for us through either of these choices — neither in stubborn *independence* nor in childish *dependence.* We will find maturity only in the third alternative — in a healthy *interdependence* on other Christians, through a fellowship where we can learn to be ourselves in an honest and loving relationship with others.

We will find maturity in a fellowship only where we can learn to be ourselves in an honest and loving relationship with others.

79

A Christian Commune

an experiment

The church
of tomorrow:
Christians are
going to go back to
basic community living
. . . where they can
communicate on a very
deep level.

on togetherness

by **Wally Howard**

*This is
a story of
fourteen Christians
who decided to move
together and share in
an experiment of
Christian community.*

To some it is "the ultimate small group." To others, "the Kingdom." Fourteen young Christians, living together in a plain brick building in Brooklyn, are experimenting with a lifestyle that has much to say to the church at large.

Three married couples and two single people moved into the building last year to fashion a "larger Christian family," sharing expenses and responsibility and a form of Christian

This article is from Faith at Work *magazine, August, 1971. Reprinted by permission.*

congregation that meets regularly for worship and organizational business. They call it "One Two Three" after the street number, or simply "The Community." The married couples are still with it and the number of singles has grown to eight.

"What is the Kingdom," one member asks, "if it isn't what we have here: a six-foot seven Chinese law student, a Jewish cab driver, a black guy from Bedford-Stuyvesant, a white couple with two kids, an interracial couple, a young couple from California, a vivacious secretary, a teacher and a college student sharing their food and Christian love with one another and with those who come in from the outside?"

This is a "small-group experience" around the clock, with all the support and challenge the term implies. "All of us need community to keep us honest, open and growing," one member explains; "we need more than a once-a-week prayer and sharing group. Here we are in vital relationship with each other every day. We can't hide our problems nor run away from conflicts. We have to deal with them."

The roots of this little community go back some ten years to the time when Bill Milliken moved into New York's Lower East Side to proclaim the good news of Christ to kids on the streets. He found that he could help young people grow strong in Christ only if he could provide better living situations for them, so he rented

an apartment and filled it with new converts. Soon there were five apartments and dozens of young people struggling together to liberate themselves from the downward tug of their environment.

Bill Milliken eventually married and moved with his wife, Jean, into a three-room apartment. "But something was missing," he recalls. Secretly he longed for the shared community he had known earlier. Jean was reluctant at first to agree to such an experiment. When she did, the Millikens, together with John and Diane McIntyre and Allan and Doris Reed, found the house in Brooklyn and moved in.

The first floor — living room, dining room and kitchen — became common rooms; the upstairs bedrooms were assigned as private quarters, to be decorated and furnished as each couple or single person chose. Meals are shared, as are expenses for rent, food, heat and light.

Each member makes his living in the outside world.

The first discovery the group made was that living together didn't automatically make them a community. Though the three couples had been working together in the Young Life mission, they found they didn't know each other as well as they had thought. With the new closeness they began to get on each other's nerves. They had expected a "honeymoon" at first, anticipating difficulties later, if at all. Instead, things started off poorly and gradually blossomed into a depth of

relationship that none would part with easily today.

"It's been the best year of my life," Bill Milliken insists. "I've lived five lifestyles — growing up at home, living alone, living with the guys on Madison Street, sharing an apartment with my wife, and living in this community — and this is the most liberating and growth-producing of all."

What about the desire for privacy and personal possessions — the two values that seem most threatened by shared living?

"There's more privacy here than in your own apartment," Diane McIntyre claims. "If people drop in on you and you want privacy, there is always someone who wants to talk. There's a community to share our visitors. Single people often like to sit and talk until late, so we can just sneak out and let them take care of guests. There's privacy if we want it."

Most wives have an unwanted kind of privacy. For instance young mothers are left at home alone for hours. For them communal living offers a new freedom. Jean Milliken was trapped much of the time in her apartment with two small children until they moved to the Brooklyn house. Now there are others who will care for her children and she is free to teach in the prep school which Young Life has initiated. "I was worried at first," Jean admits. "I didn't think people would care enough for my kids to make it possible for me to get out of the house and do something else that I wanted to do. But I find a willingness and a commitment to the kids that is hard to believe. It's good for our children to have contact with other people. They learn much more being related to a larger family," "And," Diane adds, "the community surrounds us with many gifts: humor, art, music, conversation. . . ."

Jean readily admits that her biggest fears involved her possessiveness and not wanting to be known. "It meant giving our furniture to the community. I knew some things would probably get ruined, and I was tremendously uptight. I worried about whether other people would have my standards of cleanliness. As it turned out, some of them didn't, and it has made for conflict.

"But the hardest thing to overcome was my fear of being exposed in community living. People thought of me as a great Christian woman, when actually I was quite rigid. I knew when they got to know me they might think

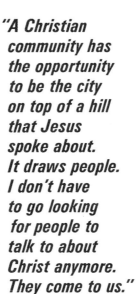

"A Christian community has the opportunity to be the city on top of a hill that Jesus spoke about. It draws people. I don't have to go looking for people to talk to about Christ anymore. They come to us."

of me as a bitch. I wanted to be flexible and I didn't want to be hung up on *things.* I wanted people to be more important than things. I saw that community living would give me the chance to deal with these hangups, so I decided I would just have to trust that people would love me in spite of myself — because love isn't real unless you can let everything hang out.'"

The result is a happy arrangement in which both men and women take turns buying groceries and preparing the evening meal, and where each member has responsibilities for cleaning and maintenance. A Wednesday night family meeting deals with any crises that arise, and a Sunday morning worship service follows brunch, or "love feast," that is shared by all.

On the practical side, the members figure that living at "One Two Three" has cut their rent by one third and reduced their grocery bills significantly. "We believe with Clarence Jordan," they say, "that 'one man's excess is another man's need,' and by sharing in this way we have more to give

away." Their goal is a community based on need, not greed.

But the greatest values of community living go beyond monetary savings — what it does for interpersonal relations, for instance. Conflicts have to be faced up to quickly and dealt with. "You can't hide from each other for long," Jean Milliken explains. "And you can solve your problems better in community. If you're hurting, others pick it up and perhaps see things more objectively.

"The situation is good for single people," she continues. "They get an idea of what married life and having children is like. We try to be honest about what it means to be married and to work out our problems in the open. The first time Bill and I did this two of the singles seemed scared to death. I checked with them afterward and found that one had never seen a fight between married couples that didn't come to blows or end up in divorce proceedings, and the other said that in his culture women just didn't stand up to their men. So I think it was good that we didn't let the problem slide until we could be alone."

Both Bill and Jean admit that community living puts greater demands on marriage, but that their own marriage is stronger for it. "I'm more keyed up about marriage than ever," Bill insists.

All the members agree that being in the community strengthens their ministry as Christians. Much of their witness grows out of what people observe of them at home. The community draws people; there's something about a shared life that attracts them. Young and old, they come from everywhere because they sense that here is a home that is open, a home where love is shared.

"When a kid comes in and sees me washing dishes, cooking a meal or changing diapers," Bill reasons, "that speaks to him about my faith. It declares that I want my wife to be free and creative, so I share the duties at home. And when you say to someone, 'Come, follow Christ,' he can grasp what you're talking about. He knows you're talking about a whole lifestyle. And that's what kids are looking for today.

"I visit a lot of college campuses and I hardly ever talk to a kid who has had a happy home. I find the younger generation haven't much hope for the family. But they're longing for community."

Bill's eyes light up when he talks about the possibilities for Christians. "Community has the opportunity to be the city on top of the hill that Jesus spoke about; the light you put on a lampstand. I don't have to go looking for people to talk to about Christ anymore. They come to us."

Bill draws a distinction between a commune and a community. "Some people have formed communes that have turned in on themselves. They spend too much time introspectively and everything gets complicated. But a true community exists for others. It pumps life out into the world. We are really committed to one another — but we're also involved out on the streets and in our jobs. To live for ourselves would be to deny Christ's values — and we're committed to his value system. I'd like to see communities like this set up all across

continued on page 87

My Own Pilgrimage

by Bill Milliken

As I reflect back on the first 17 years of my life, I see that period as a time spent strictly in Fantasyland. It was the world of material things — of seeking popularity, of getting ahead, of trying to find meaning in a surrounding atmosphere of meaninglessness. Love was shown to me basically through being given things. By the time I was 16, I had my own car and motorcycle, plus more clothes and spending money than one person needed. Getting was the central theme of life. Get ahead! Get people to love you! Get status! Get education! Get girls! Get! Get! Get! And you'll get satisfaction — happiness! This was the fantasy.

I could put on a good front (I was class president. I could hang out at the country club or the pool hall. I wrestled on the school team. In most people's eyes I really had it made). But I was lonely, insecure, and confused about who I was and where I was going. I had a deep inferiority complex, especially in the area of education. I was quiet a lot of the time, not because of "being cool" like everyone thought, but because I didn't know how to relate as a human being and felt most people didn't really want to know what was going on inside of me.

Many nights I would lie in bed and wonder what the hell life was all

*I thought I had left
my masks behind, but
all I had done was narrow
them down to two —
one was the me on the
streets, the other
was the me inside."*

about and who I was and what I was
doing here. I'd learned to protect
myself by wearing so many masks that
I wasn't sure "which face" was the
real Bill Milliken — if any of them
were. I became more and more disen-
chanted with my life and saw no
alternative. I ran away a few times
but that was just another escape from
reality. School was dull with little
challenge. I was a lousy student. I
didn't go to church much except on

special occasions and went just to
"look good." And when I did go,
church seemed phoney.

No matter how nice the houses were
we lived in, we all seemed to be living
in cocoons of escapism, loneliness,
frustration and apathy. I wanted
desperately to break out of the cocoon
but was afraid — and didn't know how.
At 17 I was fighting desperately to be
freed from something but I didn't
know what.

Things began an abrupt turnabout for
me when I went on a week-long trip
to Colorado with an organization called
Young Life. They talked about a person
named Jesus Christ as though he was
the most exciting person in the world.
I had always looked upon Jesus Christ
an an effeminate guy, wearing a dress
and carrying a sheep in his arms.
The only time I heard his name was in
a locker room at school and that
wasn't in the most positive sense.

By the end of the week I walked
off alone into the vast Rocky Mountain night knowing that I had some
important things to consider. I wrestled
to sort out all of the thoughts and
feelings swirling around in my head.
Finally I gave up the battle and
cried, "Christ, if You're real, I wish
You'd do something in my life, because I sure need it."

Upon arrival back home, I found

that this new life was full of many
unknowns. There were many questions
and few answers. I wasn't at all
sure what it meant to follow Christ.
I had never been committed to much
of anything. Commitment was a
whole new concept.

One of the pitfalls I had to face
was fitting into the "Jesus bag"
that people had defined for themselves
and me. Often I found I couldn't
be around Christians unless I was
"with it," leading a "successful life"
without problems. It became too easy
to play games and use Jesus as
another mask to hide behind rather
than allowing him to be the liberator
who would enable me to risk being
known.

I spent a few freshman years at the
University of Pittsburgh thinking
that I needed a college education.
I again became very restless and
bored. I didn't feel like wasting more
years doing that, so at the age of 20,
I left home, joined a friend of mine —
a former addict who had just been
released from jail — and moved into
a small tenement apartment in Harlem
(New York City).

I now entered another new phase.
The experiences of life on the hot,
overcrowded streets of a big city
are an adventure in themselves. But
the biggest adventure of all for me

85

was that of finding out who I was. Somehow in those early years in fantasyland, I had never been in touch with the real me. Then people who were attempting to help me in my first years of being a Christian often fed me "bad news" instead of "good news." "Bad news" in the sense that they ingrained in me that I had to be "different," which in essence really meant that I was to be like them. I learned to smile "the new smile" — to have that "victorious" look. I even started dressing straight and wearing my hair as they did. I picked up a Christian vocabulary and began talking about the "new life" much better than I was walking it. I came to the city with a fairly bad case of spiritual schizophrenia.

Out on the streets I was one kind of person — one who seemed to have it made. I had a good rap, and "sold" Jesus as the person who would solve all problems and make people "happy." The other part of me hid away in the apartment for long hours — lonely, frustrated, insecure and afraid, crying out to be loved and known.

This "bad news" had caused me to hide behind Jesus, sacrificing the knowing of myself. I was trying to love others while not yet accepting myself. After being confronted many times and called "phoney," I began to doubt whether the whole Christian thing was real or whether I was on some jive trip. I found I was angry at God, at myself and at people in general. I became very cynical and questioned everything. I wasn't sure who the real me was. I thought I'd left my masks behind, but all I'd done was narrow them down to two — one was the me on the streets, the other was the me inside. One was the so-called Christian man, the other one was a question mark. Somehow, I knew that the two

me's would have to come together or one would have to go.

The guys on the street knew I was confused and often challenged me. Finally, in desperation I invited five of the fellows who were still open to talking about God over to the apartment. For the first time, I let them know what I was thinking and what I was like. I explained my confusion. I told them I wasn't sure what I believed about God and was ready to chuck everything in order to find truth and to find out who I was.

I invited them to do this pursuing with me. We committed ourselves to each other and spent hours searching for meaning in ourselves, the Scriptures and the world around us. There were many hard encounters over the next few months, but we became closer as Christ began to heal our insides through confession to each other.

We not only changed, but had the adventure of seeing others change around us. We saw brothers and sisters starting to reach out and care for one another. We saw store-front schools develop. We were given apartments to house people who didn't have a place to stay. We saw guys and girls getting off drugs and people beginning to take their first steps in following Christ.

The most exciting "good news" for me was that I didn't have to be "different" in the way the church dictated, but that I was now free to admit who I was. If people didn't dig it, that was their problem. I wanted everybody to love me, and at times really needed them to, but I was getting to the point where I wasn't dependent on their approval for my acceptance and security. The "good news" I also discovered was that I was beginning to love myself, and in the process I became free to

give myself away to my neighbor. I was finding life by losing it.

The new life of adventure was growth-producing, painfully stretching, but I wouldn't trade it for anything. However, it has caused me to urge people to count the cost before they claim the name of the risen Christ.

"My experience on the hot, overcrowded streets of New York was an adventure in itself. But the biggest adventure of all was in finding out who I was."

continued from page 84

the country as an alternative for the kids who are drifting into communes that turn out to be sex communities or drug communities or just community for the sake of community.

"This is the church of tomorrow, I think. Christians are going to go back to basic community whether they share a house like this or move close to each other. They're going to learn to communicate on a deep level.

"A Christ-centered community lives under a new authority. We've tried for too long to live under two different value systems: the way of the world and the way of Christ. I don't think we can comprehend the power of the world to squeeze us into its mold until we form a Christian community and work to free ourselves from the false systems that oppress us.

"I was told, growing up, that it was good to get ahead, to accumulate possessions, to seek success and status. But I wasn't told what all this possessiveness and competition would do to other people: how I would have to climb over others to pull myself up, how I would deprive others by refusing to share. Now I'm learning a new value system. Success, according to Christ, is loving your neighbor, sharing your goods, giving your life away instead of hoarding it.

"In community we challenge each other in all areas of life. This in turn can challenge the community around us and eventually the world."

Is it working this way for the community in Brooklyn?

Keith Sherwood is the Jewish cab driver who moved in last February. "I drove a girl here from the airport," he explains, "and she invited me to stay for dinner. I kept coming back. I had never seen people who loved with such freedom. They reached out to me. It wasn't so much what they said as the way they treated me. I began to see a new purpose for life, and when I mentioned that I was looking for an apartment they asked, 'Why don't you move in with us?'

"I grew up in Brooklyn and always thought I was different because I didn't want to cut throats to get ahead. By society's standards I would never be a success. I was low man on the totem pole. But now I see that there are other standards, and by these I am already a success.

"I came here very fuzzy about my faith, and for a time I was the weak link in the chain. But this community is based on faith in God, and they held me up so that now I have a strong faith. As a cab driver I meet dozens of people every week. All I want to do is treat others the same way I've been treated by these Christians. Brotherhood is an infectious thing. It's almost scary."

Hollywood Church Happenings

A revolution is going on in the youth culture in goals, values and ideals . . . and the church needs to be speaking to this situation with folk music.

by Don Williams

An underground newspaper, a coffee house, rock concerts on the beach, rehabilitation houses for young people, a small printing business, a Christmas parade up Hollywood Boulevard — these are a few of the things that are happening in this well-known traditional church.

She was a teen-ager, on drugs, and pregnant. For two years she'd been living on Sunset Strip.

I was preaching the morning she wandered into Hollywood Presbyterian Church. Sharon lingered after the service; she told me of her guilt and

This story is taken from a larger article in Faith at Work *magazine, August, 1971. Reprinted by permission.*

despair and wondered if she could be forgiven.

Quite simply I shared the good news of Christ — that God loved her and forgave her. We prayed together. She came back that night and we talked some more — a couple of hours, perhaps. It was the beginning of a new life for her.

We found a place for her to stay until she had her baby, supported her in her decision to give it up for adoption. In turn, Sharon introduced me to her friends. I began to spend time on the streets of Hollywood and in hippie coffee houses, seeing the world of the youth culture for the first time.

Sharon's conversion to Jesus Christ was dramatic. My own conversion to a new style of youth ministry was just as dramatic. I discovered that a revolution was going on that shifted values, goals and ideals in the youth culture. A lot of it was negative. A lot of it was meaningful. But the church needed to get out on the streets where the youth were.

Our first effort was a coffee house. One day I spotted an old apartment

The youth minister leads
Sunday morning worship
in the patio of the church.

Members of the coffee house
folk group perform at a
nearby beach in Santa Monica.

building near the church that looked
right for the coffee house. We took
the upstairs, spent $12,000 redecorating
it — mostly with volunteer help — and
invited some musical groups. Lance
Bowen, who later became the first
full-time director, thought up the
name: The Salt Company. Taking
inspiration from Jesus' words, "You
are the salt of the earth," he saw us
as people sent to flavor the world.

More than 20,000 kids visited the
coffee house in its first four years.
Operating expenses come from dona-
tions for live musical shows on Friday
and Saturday nights. Two groups
usually perform, followed by a short
wrap-up presentation of the Gospel and
an invitation to stay and talk. During
the rest of the week The Salt Company
is open to kids who want to listen to
music, play pool, or sit and talk.

For many years Hollywood Church
has sent Christian college students
overseas on summer deputation
teams. But with the critical needs
right around us, we began to stay
within a 30 mile radius. This summer
there will be five teams — 46 students
in all — in metropolitan Los Angeles
and on various beaches where young
people congregate. We'll have concerts on the sand, gathering hundreds
of kids to listen, and we'll share our
faith in Christ and stick around as
long as anyone wants to talk.

Last summer we rented two houses
and opened them to young men in
need of a place to live. We had to
have something like this for fellows
who are accepting Christ and coming
off drugs. The Christian life can't
be lived alone. In these houses we

have a means of maximizing our effectiveness.

You say to someone, "God loves you," and you must be able to back it up. If he's hungry you have to be able to give him a meal; if he needs a place to sleep, you'd better have a bed for him. We've taken in hundreds of "crashers" this way, as well as 20 or more young men who have started back to school or to work.

It's hard for these fellows to find jobs; we try to help them. Recently we started The Salt Company, Inc. — a small business that does silk-screening, makes bumper stickers, tie-dyes T shirts, and the like. We've opened a retail store on Hollywood Boulevard and started a mail-order business.

Our newspaper, "The Alternative" — brought out in the style of the under-

ground press — is edited by a brillant young man, Rich Lang, a student at Fuller Theological Seminary and an elder in the church. Its editorial slant is different from most such papers. We're not at home with "hip" language. We don't think of Jesus as "the ultimate trip" and we don't believe one gets "high" on Jesus. Knowing Jesus is a living relationship that involves discipleship, self-denial and struggle.
We

continued on page 94

The "Jesus Freaks"

— *what's it all about?*

Among today's youth there is a tremendous return to the Bible and personal faith in Jesus Christ. One of the most striking aspects of the movement is that it is not in adult hands. The youth movements of a generation ago were all adult-led and leader-centered.

Much of today's movement is spontaneous and out of control, which is what the early Church was like. Study the Book of Acts and one systematic thing you'll learn about the Holy Spirit is that he is not systematic. Today we are seeing, in Roland Allen's famous words, "a time of the spontaneous expansion of the Church."

LOOK magazine reported that the Jesus Movement had California stamped all over it. But it's spreading rapidly. Not long ago I walked into a meeting in Wichita where more than a hundred kids were singing and praying and sharing their faith. In two months the group grew to 400.

In Seattle I looked down from the top of the Space Needle and saw a sign painted on the roof of a building: "Jesus Christ is coming soon." I went exploring and found a coffee house called The Catacombs, where hundreds of young people were gathered that night in an informal service.

This is an eschatological age. Leading ecologists warn us that within 20 years we will suffocate with pollution and eat ourselves out of existence — if we don't blow ourselves up with armaments first. It would be strange if young Christians didn't respond in kind. "The world is winding itself up. Christ is coming." And he is. But I feel concern for the pessimism and despair I see among some youths who have given up on the world. God hasn't — not yet.

It's also a very spiritual age. Kids are on a tremendous quest. On Hollywood Boulevard you find Hare Krishna chanters and Buddhist monks as well as Christians. Everyone's an evangelist for something.

Old-fashioned evangelistic services are "in," complete with altar-calls. We've come full circle. Many of the adult generation were burned by the sawdust-trail evangelist and the hellfire-and-damnation preacher. They rejected them completely. So what has happened? Their kids come along and espouse what the parents rejected.

These kids are experiencing a personal, living relationship with Jesus Christ. The inauthentic experience they found on drugs has been replaced by an authentic experience of Christ. And it's not an individualistic Christianity; it is communal. These kids are living by a new set of values and sharing their lives with one another.

Don Williams

continued from page 92

try to put substantial material into "The Alternative" and aim it at intelligent college students. Twenty thousand copies are now printed every month and distributed on nearby campuses.

Once in a while we do something special. At Christmastime we had a march on Hollywood Boulevard that drew 5,000 to 6,000 people. On Easter we marched to City Hall with banners proclaiming "Jesus Christ is alive!" It was a great way to celebrate the resurrection.

All these things have benefited the church. Many of our members, both men and women, have become involved and have gained as much as they have given. Food for our houses is provided by more than forty women on a rotating basis. On Monday nights adults and kids sit down together to study the Bible and pray — with no clergyman in attendance. The flow of communication both ways has been a revolutionizing force.

I would have to say that the changed thrust of my ministry is reflected in many ways throughout the congregation. Not only have a lot of kids on the street been changed, but the church's style of ministry is changing as well.

"Not only have a lot of kids on the street been changed, but the church's style of ministry is changing as well."

about the author

I first became interested in the subject of Christian lifestyle two years ago when I bumped into a group of young people who had been heavily influenced by a community living concept. Koinonia Farms in Americus, Georgia, was an interracial Christian community who had pooled all of their resources to live together as the early church did in the Book of Acts.

At first I found their ideas naive to the extreme. But I could not deny the fact that these young people showed more love than I had seen around in a long time. They talked about the lifestyle of Jesus as though it was something real, and the Sermon on the Mount as though it was meant for today. I decided to make a fresh study of the subject for my own life. This book is the result.

I have tried in "Rap" to give a small group enough tools so that everyone involved can make his own investigation of the Sermon on the Mount and the group can work together as a real Christian community for a few weeks. I have tried not to prejudice the outcome, but instead to leave the matter of personal application of the Scripture open to each person.

I sincerely hope that this study will be more than an academic exercise for those who undertake it. I hope that it will be the beginning of something wonderfully unique in the lifestyle of every person who dares to confront the Scripture in complete openness and obedience.

acknowledgements

The author wishes to acknowledge those who have had a part in making this book a reality: ☐ Bob Blewett for the design and art work. ☐ Gene Wieland Jr., Joel Strasser and Wally Howard for the photography. ☐ Stan Yoder, Pete Yoder, Tom Hershberger and the Mennonite Publishing House for the studio production of the book. ☐ The Oxford and Cambridge University Press for their permission to use passages from *The New English Bible,* © The Delegates of the Oxford University Press and the Syndics of the Cambridge University Press, 1961 and 1970. Reprinted by permission. ☐ American Bible Society for their permission to quote from *Good News for Modern Man, Today's English Version,* © 1966, American Bible Society. ☐ The Paulist Press for their permission to quote from *Dawn Without Darkness,* © 1971, The Missionary Society of St. Paul the Apostle in the State of New York. ☐ Faith at Work for their permission to reprint two articles from *Faith at Work* magazine, © Faith at Work. ☐ Harper and Row Publishers for permission to quote from *Reshaping The Christian Life,* © Harper and Row.